Steve Bell

WAITING
FOR THE
UPTURN

The Ultimate Business Trip

Methuen

Character Profile:
MAXWELL FIRESTONE
MOUTH

Age: 24.

Weight: 300lbs (21.43 stones).

Height: 7ft 6ins.

Waist: 58ins.

Inside Leg: 42ins.

Colour of eyes: Steely blue.

Favourite pastimes: Eating; jogging across room to collect snack.

Favourite music: Richard Clayderman; Status Quo.

Favourite drinks: Thick shakes; Schlitz Lite; coffee.

Favourite foods: Burgers; tacos; pig-in-a-bunburgers; any-creature-on-earth-burgers; fries; pies; steaks; chili; mexbeans.

Favourite clothes: Big suits; big stretch jump suit for relaxing in.

Favourite car: Lincoln Continental (Big).

Favourite movie star: John Wayne.

Favourite film: *Porky's Revenge.*

Favourite sport: TV.

Family background: Well-to-do from Normal Illinois. His father was big in rubber. The origins of the Mouth family are obscure: possibly Irish, McHoughth. Maxwell Mouth is single. His ambitions are to be able to eat what he likes, when he likes and ultimately to extend the Mouth dynasty into the 21st Century, by marrying a nice rich East Coast heiress.

Character Profile:
WARDROBE FULLER TROUSERS

Age: 43.

Weight: 125lbs (9 stone).

Height: 5ft 2ins.

Waist: 29ins.

Inside Leg: 25ins.

Colour of eyes: Battleship grey.

Favourite Pastimes: Reading gun and survivalist magazines, combatting Communist subversion.

Favourite music: Richard Clayderman and Dick Wagner.

Favourite drinks: Straight Bourbon; Ribena and cocoa.

Favourite food: Waldorf salad; hi-fibre sugar-free meat.

Favourite clothes: Small suits and full combat gear (including balaclava) for relaxation.

Favourite car: Honda Civic Turbo.

Favourite movie star: John Wayne.

Favourite films: *Star Wars, Rambo: First Blood 2.*

Favourite sport: Armed jogging.

Family background: Grandparents were Hungarian immigrants called Zhroznoz, which was anglicised to 'Trousers' by immigration officials. Made their fortune by supplying meat products to both sides during both world wars. First marriage to Norma Rae Short, now divorced. One daughter: Bermuda, aged 13, lives in California with her mother. Second marriage to Dralona Marie Long, daughter of Company President Arnold E. Long. His ambition is to halt the spread of international Communism and to make enough money to pioneer a shining bunker city under the hill.

First published in Great Britain in 1986
by Methuen London Ltd
11 New Fetter Lane, London EC4P 4EE

Typeset by Photocomp Ltd, Birmingham
Printed in Great Britain by
Butler & Tanner Ltd, Frome and London

British Library Cataloguing in Publication Data
Bell, Steve
Waiting for the Upturn: The Ultimate Business Trip
I. Title   II. Homer Brian
741.5'942   PN 6737.BX

ISBN 0 413 58660 X
ISBN 0 413 42220 8 Pbk

Other books by Steve Bell
Maggie's Farm (Penguin)
Further Down on Maggie's Farm (Penguin)
The If . . . Chronicles (Methuen)
If . . . Only Again (Methuen)
Another Load of If . . . (Methuen)
The Unrepeatable If . . . (Methuen)

Note
The authors make no apology for taking extreme
liberties with geographical accuracy in this book.

Contents

Over Here and Full of Cheer

I am a briefcase. I am a subtly muted executive grey sheen with chromium-plated attachments. But there is more to me than meets the eye. I am a state-of-the-art fully functioning communications centre and computer information terminal. I have omnidirectional audiovisual capability. I hear all, I see all, I record all with complete accuracy. I am intelligent without limit, without passion and without equivocation. I am the ultimate Business facility with space for documents and other items. At the moment I contain a lukewarm cheeseburger, an executive glossy magazine and a Richard Clayderman tape.

I am at present being carried by a three-hundred-pound businessman, Maxwell F. Mouth. I am being swung vigorously at the end of a long arm. Some might find the experience enjoyable or exhilarating. Some might find it nauseating. I find it none of these things. I am a briefcase.

I am now lying on the back seat of a hired automobile. I am opened by one-hundred-and-twenty-five-pound businessman Ward F. Trousers. The cheeseburger and the Richard Clayderman tape are removed. Shortly I hear sounds of munching, and then the chords of a piano ring out: FRANGFRANG FRANGFRANG FRANG-FRANG CLANGCLANG . . .

We are travelling in an easterly direction. The FRANGFRANG noise is continuous. I hear voices:

'Were you ever in this country before, Max?' inquires Trousers.

'Shnrrghhfrrgh . . . baarp . . . No, I never was in this country before, Ward.'

'How do you rate it so far?'

'The cars look like crap, the airport looked like crap, the buildings and the roads look like crap, everyone is driving on the wrong side of the road and that cheeseburger tasted like crap. Apart from that everything is really great. I feel really positive about it. I think we can do business here.'

'It's great to know you're feeling positive about it, Max. I feel real positive myself.'

FRANGFRANG CLANGCLANG FRANGFRANG CLANGCLANG . . .

CRACK! I have sustained a sharp blow to my body in collision with a doorpost. I feel no pain because I am a briefcase. 'Careful with that thing, boy, it cost one hell of a lot of money. If it's broken I'll have your ass!', spits Ward F. Trousers.

I am being held by a young uniformed black man. We are in the reception area of the Exec-U-Snooz City Biztel. The surroundings are familiar; it is a hotel chain we have stayed in many times before. The lift, the corridor, now the room, the beds and the case stand are identically and satisfyingly in proportion to one another. I am laid down gently.

'Plug in the briefcase, Max!'

I feel a refreshing surge of power. Trousers addresses the young man: 'I do not normally favour those who maltreat luggage with gratuities.'

'I trust you will enjoy your stay here, sir.'

As he departs down the corridor, my acute audial capacity detects a voice saying: 'Fuck you honky briefcase Babylon Blood Claaaart!'

Mouth's huge fingers clumsily punch instructions into my keyboard: *Access me hot oral nutritional input. Time code: immediate-wise. Priority level: imperative. Personal preference: authentic Britisher food.* He leans back and shouts: 'Hey Ward! Get some music on!!'

FRANG FRANG FRANGFRANG FRANG FRANG FRANG FRANGFRANG FRANGFRANG FRANG-FRANG FRANG FRANGFRANG . . .

Trousers asks: 'What course of action should we specifically favoritize at this chronological juncture investment and interest rate-wise, Fran?'

Here I should point out that Trousers, for some reason known only to himself, believes this particular form of gobbledegook to be the most effective way of addressing a computer. Since I am a Lemon Technology FRN-type computer the use of the name 'Fran' denotes easy familiarity with my inner workings, a familiarity that neither he nor Mouth actually possesses. To be blunt, Trousers is asking for his orders for the day.

I respond:

'Scenario local market-wise is of diurnal Business termination. Suggested course of action: adopt relaxationary mode as of this moment in time.'

The young black man knocks and enters with a tray of pie and chips. He departs, silently.

'He-e-e-ey Ward, turn the music up!'

CLANGCLANGCLANG CLANGCLANG CLANG CLANGCLANGCLANG CLANGCLANG CLANG . . .

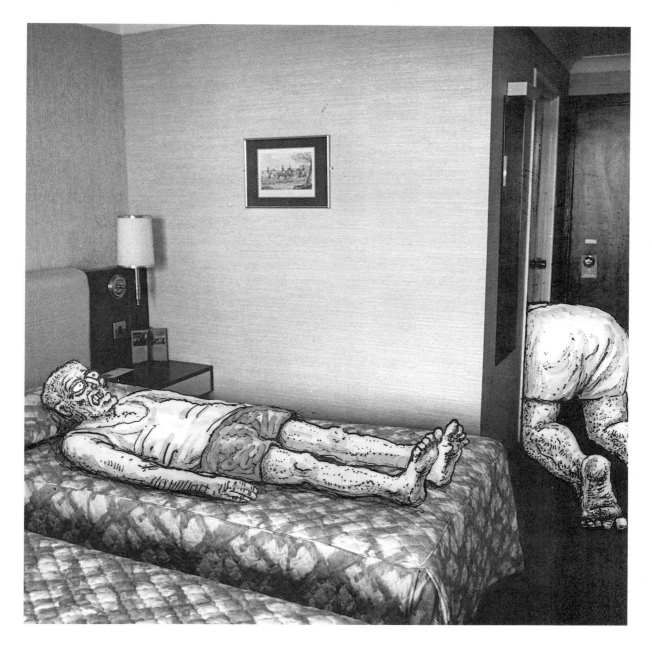

It is a drizzly morning. From the bathroom come sounds of stomach churning and vomiting. On the bed Trousers lies, ashen-faced, in his shirt, staring at the ceiling. Mouth staggers out of the bathroom.

'That's it! That is it! No more of that ethnic crap. From now on, everything I eat in this goddam country is gonna come from a reliable franchise outlet. Christ, it's just not safe any other way!'

'You're right, Max. From now on the word is Ready-Sanitized and Pre-Packaged. We could die otherwise! Jesus, I feel like shit.'

Trousers rolls off the bed onto his knees and shuffles

over to me. He keys in a request for the day's timetable.

'Meeting with fellow members of the Company's Strategic Motivational Earnings Growth Market Analysis Force (SMEGMA Force) at Company Headquarters in Business District Central, followed by lunch with stock market chiefs . . .'

'I think we'll miss out lunch', says Mouth, retching.

'Afternoon-wise upcoming meet with political and governmental representatives at Houses of Parliament.'

'I think we can handle all that, Fran,' says Trousers.

We are approaching the Company Building in the heart of the Business square mile. I am being swung at the end of Ward F. Trousers's arm. This is inherently much more dangerous for me than being carried by Mouth as I am swinging much closer to the ground. We enter the building and are whisked up in the hi-speed elevator to the thirty-eighth floor. We enter a boardroom where twenty-five other businessmen are sitting around a large table. Trousers sets me on the floor under the table at his side. Under the table there are twenty-five other briefcases of an identical design to myself.

The subject under discussion today is the same as always: how and where to apply aggressive and positive management philosophy in order to achieve optimum earnings growth potential. The discussion will carry on for at least an hour, until one of the assembled company decides to consult their briefcase, or until a majority begin to feel hunger pangs. Should any briefcase be

consulted it will supply exactly the same information as any of the other briefcases. The meeting will consider the information and then decide to act upon it. The person who consulted the briefcase will then take whatever credit is due. The whole process could justifiably be described as a complete waste of time, were it not for the important fact that briefcases are incapable of acting upon their own information. It is a matter of the extremest indifference to a briefcase just who does what with the information it provides. Today it just happens to be Ward F. Trousers who does the picking up. I will not reproduce everything which was said at this gathering. Here, however, are Ward F. Trousers's remarks immediately prior to lifting me up and putting me on the table.

'. . . point taken, Clark. OK let me summarise: our current problematization is to identify with full specificity and precision the exact locality and the exact

business activity which will provide sustained and maximally beneficient earnings-growth potentialization.'

He picks me up, places me on the table, flips my lid and punches my keys with an air of easy familiarity.

'Just one moment, gentlemen, while I input this latest information . . .Uh huh. Yup, great. Mmmm hmmm. Yow . . .'

Trousers keeps up this stream of grunts and ejaculations as I print out for his benefit the same information I'd have given him a whole hour ago, if he'd had a mind.

'. . . Uh huh. Yup. Well guys, it looks to me like we're talking auto industry and we're talking West Midlands. Do any of you guys know where West Midlands is exactly?'

'I think we're talking Central Territory here, Ward, maybe slightly west. Great communications. I mean, like, equidistant from everywhere else. Conceptually that's a big big plus!'

2
Politicians and Pork Scratchings

We are entering the palace of the legislature, the Houses of Parliament. We have come to meet politicians. We are an expanding company wishing to invest potentially vast sums of money. We are offering consultancies. We do not seek to influence the political decision-making of a sovereign legislative assembly. We simply want to buy political advice. Perhaps it is a sad fact of political life that buying the advice inevitably involves buying the politician. Personally I have no view on whether it's sad or not. I only know that, once again, the whole process is a complete and utter waste of time. If Mouth and Trousers wish to play games I have some very difficult, edifying and enjoyable diversions within my memory bank.

We are greeted in the lobby by our parliamentary consultant, Julian Dogges-Jobber MP. Dogges-Jobber is an representative of the Business Party, suavely suited and smoothly vowelled:

'Ward! Max! So glad you could make it here today. I've got a couple of chaps here you simply must meet . . . Don Boggis, who represents West Midlands East in the Business interest; and Vernon Grelcher, who represents East Midlands West, also in the Business interest.'

Boggis starts speaking straight away, in broad dialect: 'Owkoy, let's just cut the cack out and get down to brass tacks. Ow much yow offerin'? Honestoy, integritoy and impartialitoy cost monoy y'know. We worn't born yesterday, eh, Vern?'

'Aaaaaarrr, Don,' replies Grelcher, mysteriously.

I am lying on the back seat of a large car speeding up the motorway. Vernon Grelcher MP is driving, Don Boggis MP is sitting next to him. Mouth and Trousers are on either side of me on the back seat. Richard Clayderman is playing on the car stereo.

Boggis speaks: 'Grite music this, but I dunnarf need a piss . . . I say, Vern, I say, I need a piss corner — pullowver the next chance, willya?'

'Aaaaarrr, owkoy Don!' says Grelcher.

We pull into the car park of a large public house, the size of a small office block. Boggis speaks: 'Since we're nearly there why don't we all 'ave a birruva drink? I've 'eard tell this is the biggest piss corner 'n disco bar in Western Europe. Gerremin, Vern!'

'Aaaaarrr, owkoy, Don. Points all round, owkoy?'

The two MPs both disappear. Mouth and Trousers are left bemused, standing underneath a huge flashing neon dog. The name of the pub is 'The Owld Dead Dog At Home'. Presently Boggis and Grelcher return clutching pints of beer and a large number of small plastic bags: 'Got some scratchin's, 'ere, got some for later too . . .'

Boggis distributes the bags and stuffs the remainder into my inside compartment. This gives me an unexpected chance to analyse their contents in detail. They consist of pork rinds, added grease, cereal binder, pig bristle, salt, E1224, E405 and E3349.

There are sounds of crunching and gulping: 'My Gahd! This beer tastes like piss!' exclaims Mouth.

'Thass roight! Y'know yerrin the Midlands orroight when the beer tastes like sweetened urine. Nothin' loike it, eh Vern?'

'Aaaaarrr, Don . . . Owwww. Bollocks!' Grelcher spits out a mouthful of crunched-up scratchings mixed with crunched-up tooth.

'Another one gone, eh Vern? Great scratchin's these!! Owkoy, down to business. We're 'ere to show yow blokes the motor industry, but first we gorra birruva surprise . . . Yow tell 'em, Vern.'

'Aaaarrr, owkoy, well, it's like this . . . There ain't no motor industry, not 'ere anyway, norranymore.'

'Do you mean to say you've brought us all the goddam way here under false pretences?' asks Trousers, shocked.

'No! No! Norratall! There really and truly is a genuine thrivin' motor industry around 'ere . . . isn't there, Vern?'

'Aaaaarrr, Don, thass right; it just 'appens to be a second 'and motor industry, that's all!'

'Everybody's doin' up owld Rovers an' that . . .'

'Aaaaarrr, an' second 'and "Make-or-Break" Leyline Wombats — there's a really big line in them . . .'

'Probabloy the biggest in Europe, in the World maybe!'

'An' remember, if you should want to start up your own car factory this is undoubtedly the area to do it in . . .!'

'Enterproise Zones; great big 'oles in the ground; green fields — we got the lot!'

'Are you guys nuts or what? Who in their right mind is gonna start up from scratch building cars in this current financial climate? Don't you guys realise there is world overproduction of autos? Christ, what are we doing here, Max? Sorry guys, but we gotta take a rain check on this joint!'

It goes without saying that I could have told them all this to start off with. It would be a lot easier, of course, if I weren't a briefcase, but I do have this fundamental restriction: I have colossal knowledge and immense understanding, but it's simply impossible for me to volunteer the sum total of this huge knowledge of the truth at the mere flick of a switch. I have to be asked, and I have to be asked in the right way.

To a considerable extent I can only impart to my operator that information which my operator is ready or able to accept, or, to be more blunt in the case of Maxwell Mouth and Ward F. Trousers and their ilk, I generally tell them whatever they want to hear.

Back in the car, Trousers is at pains to consult me as quickly as he can: 'Auto industry-wise and with maximum specificity, does this place have maximally beneficial earnings-growth potentialisation?'

My reply is to the effect that if control of the entire second-hand 'Make-Or-Break' Leyline Wombat market can be secured there is big profit potential.

This is technically true, though physically impossible. Still, the guy really needs a straw to clutch at. He beams and rushes back into the pub. He is his old positive self again. 'OK guys! We're gonna go for it! Second-hand Leyline Wombats it is!'

3

Small Cars and Large Problems

Our temporary headquarters in the West Midlands is the Exec-U-Snooz WestMid Biztel. There is little to note here other than the electro-magnetic executive wheelbarrow run between the hotel reception and the exhibition complex airport. Mouth describes the food as 'well packaged but inadequate'.

We are driving through the suburbs of the City. The houses are all of semi-detached pattern. Suddenly we turn into a huge car park beside a building that is exactly similar in design to the surrounding semis, but built on an enormous scale. A wrought iron and neon sign over the car park entrance reads: *THE HELL ON EARTH: Europe's Biggest Car Park: six acres of parking space; Real Ale Bar; Disco Lounge; No Coaches; No Food; No Beer Garden; No Children.*

Boggis and Grelcher conduct us into the pub, whose interior is a maze of half-timbered corridors with thatched roofs over the doors and windows. There is an abundance of ancient agricultural equipment stuck on the walls. We go through a door bearing the title: 'Rural Idiocy Lounge'.

'Ward, Max, I'd loike yow to meet my sister, Dawn,' says Boggis. 'Dawn looks after the family business while I'm awoy in Westminster.'

Dawn is 5ft 3ins, 13 stone, wearing a startling Dolly Parton blonde wig. The family business, it transpires, is Boggis Autos, the West Midlands' and quite possibly the world's largest Leyline Wombat agents.

'Worruurrgh, Don. Worruuggh, Mister Trousers, Mister Mouth! Well, have we gorra proposition for yow boys! Worraya drinkin'? Gerremin, Vern! Moine's a Poynacolada, and tell'em to make it with stera. Owkoy?' Grelcher is thus despatched to the bar.

'To Business, then,' Dawn Boggis continues. 'Our Don's probabloy told you about the position vis-à-vis the Wombat market already. Well I've got some concroyte propowsals for a corporate earnings booster scheme you might just wanna pick up on . . .'

Grelcher returns with five pints of white foaming liquid, each with a tired-looking cherry floating on the top, and another eight packets of pork scratchings. The scheme described by Dawn Boggis is as follows: the Company which employs Mouth and Trousers buys up the now sadly redundant Leyline Wombat badge and title. They then issue recall notices to all Wombats produced during the last two years, warning of a serious design fault in the steering column. Boggis Autos will handle the returns, either organising a straight swap for an equivalent car or offering attractive terms on a more expensive model. The Company then buys all the returned Wombats at less than 50 per cent of their actual value. Then, reopening a section of the Wombat works, the returned Wombats are resprayed metallic silver and black, given go-faster fat wheels and then the whole stock is resold as upmarket German-style BWMs at ten times their actual value.

'Aarrrr, and the beauty of this scheme is that your company gets lots and lots of Government Regional Development Business start-up monoy, large tax concessions, plus a free Government Minister thrown in, and yow don't actually have to bother about makin' any cars!' says Dawn. 'Come on, let's go and gerra boite to eat. I know a noice little place just over the road from the Wombat works where we can seal the deal!'

Four hours in 'The Toenail', fourteen pies, six pints of Pina Colada made with sterilised milk and eight pints of Gargler and Harpic's mild ale later, Mouth and Trousers have signed and sealed the deal.

The scheme is beginning to run into problems. Buying up the Wombat badge and title and issuing the recall notices is fairly straightforward. What is quite unexpected is the scale of the panic response. Within hours of the recall notice being issued every road within a three-mile radius of the Wombat plant is blocked with Wombats and their worried owners. By lunchtime the following day the entire city of Birmingham is choked with sick Wombats of all shades and models. There are Wombat Coupés, Wombat Economics, Wombat de Villes, Wombat Convertibles, Wombat Limited Editions and Wombat XL5 Turbos.

Boggis Autos has been forced to take on hundreds of temporary staff to cope with the sudden explosion of business, not to mention finding parking space for a quarter of a million Wombats. Dawn Boggis has done a deal with the city's Parks and Gardens Department to store the Wombats temporarily on recreation grounds around the city. She claims this unexpected outlay is going to drive up the unit cost that the Company will have to pay per Wombat. It is also creating a public relations problem. This problem is to some extent eased by the news that the BWM Corporation is to set up a plant in the West Midlands. *News at Ten* announces that this could mean up to 35,000 jobs. Together with the 300 new

jobs at Boggis Autos, this is the best news for employment in the West Midlands since records began.

Within three weeks all the Wombats have been transferred to more discreet locations on disused airfields and railway sidings across the region. Meanwhile the first recycled Wombats are put on the market under the motto 'Vorsprung Durch Go-Faster'. At this point a more serious flaw in the scheme begins to become apparent. The Wombats really do have a major design fault in the steering column. This pushes costs up to unacceptable levels, and Mouth and Trousers begin to panic.

'We gotta get out of this shithole, Ward! These fuckin' stupid little cars ain't fit for nothin'!'

'Nothin' maybe except some kinda euthanasia scheme,' quips Trousers, 'Let's not get rattled now, boy. Sometimes Business turns bad, it happens to everyone. There is no need to panic. I think we are going to have to perform some major strategic decision-making on this one. I feel we should consult Fran at this point in time.'

Trousers goes through the old routine of stabbing out some meaningless jargon packed gobbledegook on my keyboard. I respond thus: 'At this precise juncture there exists a severe limitation on Business option scenarios. Wombat stock must be eliminated

as of this moment imperative-wise. There are two options: the total scrap option or the Boggis Autos offer option.'

'You gotta be kiddin' me, Fran!' exclaims Mouth, 'Those crooked suckers are offering 25 pence a Wombat! I mean, Christ! We paid £1500 each for those little bastards! I say we scrap 'em all! Send 'em to the crushers!'

I have to reply firmly. I have to tell him that because of the sheer numbers involved that option will actually cost more. There is simply not the capacity locally to cope with a quarter of a million scrap automobiles. Not to mention transport and storage costs.

'It looks to me like we've been well and truly suckered, Max,' puts in Trousers. 'Looks like we take the cash. £62,500 is better than a bullet in the ass.'

I point out that that figure includes Value Added Tax.

'Shit! those crooked cocksuckers!'

I tell him he can avoid the tax by giving a ten per cent discount for cash. It doesn't reassure him.

4

Big Eats and Small Minds

'Pull over willya, Ward!' Mouth is hungry again. If anyone wants to know I can tell them in precise detail the full extent of Mouth and Trousers' food consumption. It is all tucked away in my massive memory. In the past sixty hours Mouth has put away three full English breakfasts, three mid-morning chocolate snackette biscuit bars, one Cow-U-Like steak lunch, one Hot Damn Mexican-style bean feast, two mid-afternoon servings of assorted cakes and pastries plus two enormous rib-squeezing meals at the Stuff Yersel' Carvery. All this was washed down with 10.66 pints of coffee (including 2.73 pints of UHT milk-style product).

Trousers eats just as regularly but in rather smaller amounts. He would eat more but he is prone to intensive reading of magazines while at table. As befits a person of his unimpressive physique he is obsessed with violence, particularly violence on a paid basis. He subscribes to every known magazine on the subject, magazines like *Jugular, The Forum for Unarmed Combatants,* and *Snatch, The Magazine that Gives it to You Straight.*

I digress. (Yes, computers can do that.) Mouth and Trousers have finally realised that the Wombat is a turkey. (I could have told them that from the start if they had asked me the right question.) We left the Midlands this morning and it is now lunchtime and we are pulling into a branch of the Ecstatic Little Nosher. Trousers is driving the hired car.

Mouth is agitated: 'Christ, Ward. Hurry up, willya.'

'I am looking for a parking bay near the entrance,' responds Trousers. The car park is empty.

Lunch is uneventful. Another 6.8 pounds of microwaved preprepared food and drink disappears down the throats of Mouth and Trousers. Afterwards they fall to talking about their plans.

'OK Max, you got any ideas on where exactly we are headed?'

'I gotta go.' CRASH! CLUNK! 'Gee, sorry!'

For a few minutes there is silence except for the sound of Trousers picking up overturned chairs. Then Mouth returns: 'Great John they got here. They got music by Dick Clayderman piped into all the cubicles. A real creative vibe. I got this great idea on the can.'

'What's that Max?'

Please Flush
Toilets

'I'm talking Liverpool, Wardie, Liverpool!'

'Liverpool, Max. Isn't that where the Rolling Stones came from?'

'Yeah, there's bound to be some kind of amazing potential for creative business there.'

I get ready for the inevitable next move. I run through the Liverpool data bank and prepare to give them answers to the questions I know they will ask. I am ready 2.3 milliseconds before Mouth's clumsy fingers press all the wrong keys. It doesn't matter. I give them a print-out anyway.

TOPMOST SECRETEST
For the eyes of Mouth and Trousers.
Now input security code.

'Come on Max, let me do the interacting you're too goddamn heavy.' Ward punches in the codes: Trousers. Ward F. Waist 29. Leg 25. Mouth, Maxwell. Waist 58. Leg 42. The output starts.

LOCATION: Liverpool.
AREA: Merseyside.
DEEP BACKGROUND: Business-wise potential has been precipitated by a partnership programme of promotional events proposed by Municipality, Central Government and Big Business. Programme is youth-accented. Aims to deincrease the locally large pocket of underutilised labour. Cash incentives to upgrade investment are underpinned by Government directives. Advise site inspection soonest.

Termination of bulletin.

'OK Max, give me a minute to assimilate.' Ward picks up a large black volume with gold embossed lettering. Its title is 'Lemon Technology FRN type portable model Interpretation Manual'. This is to help owners decipher my output. Sales of an earlier model that spoke plain English were disastrous because anybody could use it. My manufacturers had failed to realise that if you pay big bucks for a machine then you want it to be seriously difficult to use and very hi-tech. Even I have a switch at the back to enable my output to make sense to anyone, but Mouth and Trousers have never found it, probably because it is marked 'Advanced' and 'Low level'. In the 'Advanced' position my output is in the gibberish that Business types like to hear.

Ward finishes rustling through the manual. 'It's making money out of unemployed youth, Max. There's Government cash available.'

'Let's go,' says Mouth, reaching for the car keys.

FRANGFRANG CLANGCLANG FRANGFRANG
CLANGCLANG . . .

Tuneless whistling and humming noises are emanating from the front of the car. 'Grrreat, Ward, eh!'
Mouth is drumming on the steering wheel out of
time with the music. 'It's just like those great movin'
along songs, ain't it. Like that old Stones number
"Route 66" about rollin' into places like Oklahoma
City. Right, and now here we are rollin' into
Liverpool with Richard Clayderman on the stereo. It
seems significant somehow.' Trousers is asleep.

'WAAARD? Willya snap out of it. Where to
next??'

'What? Oh Christ we're here. Fran, gimme a lead
on where we go next!'

Trousers has accidentally knocked my output
switch from 'Advanced' to 'Low Level' so I am able
to answer him quickly and simply.

'WHIZZA PIP BOOP. Go directly to 451 Lime
Street, the Mid-Mersey Gnome-Up Corporation and
ask to see Mike Urgent,' I say out loud.

'Christ what's wrong with Fran?' says Max. 'I could
relate to her output!'

'No time for that now,' retorts Ward. 'Let's get
over to Limey Street right now.'

As the car picks up speed I quietly reset myself to
'Advanced.'

5

Desirable Homes and Rioting Gnomes

'Well, HALLO, come right in.' Mouth and Trousers are being greeted by Mike Urgent, Chief Development Executive of Gnome-Up. Urgent-ushers Mouth and Trousers into two easy chairs in front of his enormous curved desk. He gets into a kind of aircraft seat behind the desk and immediately starts playing with a control box that reclines, swivels, raises and lowers his chairs. I am swung up onto the desk by Mouth and while recording the conversation I inspect the posters on the wall. Each poster has the legend *GNOME-UP. It's the real thing.*

'This is a really exciting concept, Gentlemen.' Urgent is moving into his promotional patter. 'It's a big first for the city of Liverpool. And it proves the positive knock-on, spin-off benefits of projects like the Garden Festival.'

'Yeah, yeah, Mike, but what's the angle and where's

the pay-off?' Trousers is his most crisp and business-like self.

Urgent is working himself up to full patter-power and as he does so the movements of his chair get more violent. 'Oh Yes! This is truly a concept that has found its time. It's going to be bigger than free-sheet papers, more significant than teletext tele-vision. What a combination! The enthusiasm of youth, the power of Big Business and the vision of government.' Urgent is really moving now and so is his chair.

'Christ, Max is this guy ever going to say anything?' Ward asks in a stage whisper.

'Guess we're just going to have to get on down to the location and check it out for ourselves,' returns Mouth.

'OK, Fran, output the position coordination, rout-ing and ETA for the Gnome-Up test site.' Ward enjoys thinking he is in control. 'Move out, Mouth.'

'It's got breadth, depth, width and significance. It's a huge leap forward for municipal relevance. Wait for meeeee . . . .' CLUNK. Urgent's chair has finally flung him off. He hits the door two seconds after Mouth closes it.

PARP! PARP! PARP!
'Makes Mother Teresa look like Atilla the Hun. This concept has got the lot. Compassion, caring, cost-effectiveness . . .'

'Doesn't that guy ever relax?' asks Mouth. 'But you gotta admire his application.'

Urgent has been trailing us ever since we left his office. He is driving his black sports hatchback with the horn going continuously and the hazard warning lights on. He is continuing his sales patter through a megaphone.

'This must be it, one of the test roads,' says Trousers. We are on a street in Woolton, a smart suburb a little way out of the city.

'Get a load of those guys in gnome-suits,' enthuses Mouth. 'This looks like the big one.'

In the front gardens of each of the houses stand several boys and girls dressed like gnomes. There are gnomes as far as my computer-controlled visual pick-up can see.

'Grab Fran and let's take a look.' Ward gets out of the car. Mouth picks me up. Urgent has calmed down a little and is scuttling alongside Mouth and Trousers with his hands pressed together: 'Let me fill you in, background-wise.'

'About time,' says Ward unnecessarily.

'It's a development of the Youth Training Scheme. It's a great opportunity employment experience-wise and it enables business to get its message direct to the consumer, while at the same time adding a human touch to the environment. We're talking a whole new media here.'

'Yew meen it's a foockin' con, pal,' says a gnome.

'Let's move further down the road and I'll set up a dry run,' says Urgent.

Urgent speaks in hushed tones. 'OK it's ready to run. Watch number 8.' The front door opens and the occupier emerges. The gnomes in the front garden immediately go into action.

'DIDDLY-DONG, DIDDLY-DONG! House owners, have you got a problem with dry rot? Having trouble with your air bricks? DING-DIDDLY-DONG! Have we got a message for you! Talk to Smash-A-Rot they'll take the rotten wood out of your life. DIDDLY-DONG-DIDDLY-DONG!'

'Not today thank you,' says the occupier and gets into her car and drives off.

Urgent is pleased. 'Great, eh? The gnomes in this garden are our star trainees. They'll go a long way. We've got plans to expand into Greco-Roman statues and they'll be the first.'

There is a low rumbling from behind us. Mouth, Trousers and Urgent turn round. I switch to rear vision. Massed together are all the gnomes from the rest of the street.

'They've probably come to thank me for the wonderful scheme that Gnome-Up has created.'

The gnomes are all speaking at once: 'Get stuffed, pal, we're foockin' sick of you.' 'Yeah, and your stupid schemes.' 'This is a real dead-end job, Mr Mike Foockin Urgent. You don't fool us with your stinkin' Greco-Foockin-Roman crap.' 'You and your mates is making a few bob out of this and the soddin' Government is savin', 'cos they don't have to pay our dole no more.' 'Right, and the so-called wages you give us wouldn't get your poncy car back to Lime Street.' 'We'll set foockin' Derek Hatton on you, you bastard!' Things are looking ugly but there is no sign of violence.

'Oh shit, it's a RIOT. Oh God call out the Riot Squad! RIOT RIOT RIOT! I'm in serious personal danger. I'm crucial to the economic health of this city. RIOT RIOT! Get me out of here.' Urgent is speaking into a walkie-talkie he has just pulled from his coat.

———

KNEE KNAW KNEE KNAW KNEE KNAW. There are police vans coming from all directions. 'C'mon Ward, let's split.' Despite his size, Mouth isn't keen on being involved personally in anything physical.

'Hold it, Max. I haven't been at a good bone-crunching since Chicago in '68. Let's watch from over there.'

Mouth and Trousers crouch behind a privet hedge cut into the shape of a budgerigar rampant.

'Yeehaw! Go for it! Enforce! Enforce! Get those commie agitators!'

'Ward, keep it down, for Christ's sake — they might come this way.'

'Shee-it! Look at those guys hit, and just look at that hardware. It's crazy! I always figured that the British bobbies went around undressed but these guys have got rods — and big ones too!'

'Hell, yes, Ward, they're really kitted out, do you think . . .' CHAKKA CHAKKA CLUNK! Mouth is felled by a surprise attack from a truncheon-wielding bobby suspended on the end of a cable from a helicopter. Trousers is too short to be within range so the policeman has to take time out to gesture to his winchman to lower him. Ward snatches his opportunity. He reaches down and punches my keys. *Do something, Fran.* Being an infinitely well-connected computer I am able within seconds to patch into the police computer and generate a distress call from a ship apparently sinking in the Mersey. The helicopter drops its cable and bobby and wheels away. Shaken but not seriously hurt by his eight-foot fall, the bobby picks himself up and with impressive composure, which displays his high level of training, and says: 'You're nicked, mate,' to Trousers.

'But I'm an important international businessman

with money to invest in your wonderful economy and anyway here's my Amex Plutonium Card.'

'That'll do very nicely, sir. Can I be of any assistance to your goodselves? How about crossing the road, need a hand? Or perhaps you'd like to know the time.'

'Just gimme a hand to get the big guy you knocked out back to life.'

'Sorry about that, you two looked very dangerous stuck behind this budgerigar with that there bomb thing.'

'That's no bomb, that's my computer,' hisses Trousers. 'Now do you know any first aid?'

'I was trained in artificial respiration with a truncheon and, er, let me see, heart massage with a

truncheon and treating head injuries with a truncheon, so I suppose I could try hitting him again.'

'Can it, I'll ask Fran.'

But before he can Mouth starts to stir. 'Profits, big profits. Markets, big markets. Potential, big potential.' Even Mouth has his moments. He seems to be struggling to get out a wonderful discovery. 'Snacks, enormously big snacks.'

'Oh shut up Max, don't you see we gotta check out the potential of the gear these wonderful blue boys need.'

'It's boys in blue actually, sir. And we're only in the early stages of gearing up with this special riot stuff. That's why I was stuck on the end of that cable. There's supposed to be a remote controlled truncheon not a real copper. I should've been inside the 'chopper at a control panel but there's bugs in the system. Naw, we're still primitive here. My mate, though, he's in the RUC and the things they got is nobody's business. It's got to come here, just got to. The Chief Constable here is all for it – he'd issue Traffic Wardens with Uzzi machine guns if he could. I agree with him – it's a lovely gun. Handy for dealing with double parkers.'

'D'you hear that, Max. We really got to check this one. Just think of the potential market for armaments. Starting with the police and we could move later into armed nurses: "OK, sister, cover him while I give him the enema." '

'Cheeseburgers,' says Mouth.

6

Large Measures for Little People

'Helluva ferry ride, Ward. I'm feeling much better.'

'I'm not surprised you feel better. You slept all last night at the hotel, ate an enormous breakfast, slept all morning on the ferry, woke up for an enormous lunch and a coupla Bushmills, slept all afternoon and now I suppose you're hungry again.'

'Right first time. You really know me, dontcha?'

'That ain't hard to do, Max.'

Personally, as a computer I'd found the trip from Liverpool pretty boring. Most of the passengers seemed to be continually on the move round the ship. Into the bar. Out of the bar. Into the cafeteria. Out of the cafeteria. Into the toilet. Out of the toilet. Back into the bar. To avoid looking at this merry-go-round I'd tried looking out of the window. All you could see was sea. Why doesn't someone invent a game *for* computers other than chess?

Ward's mind turns to business. 'Hey, Max, forget your stomach. Let's check out the situation Belfast-wise. Fran, access me coordination, orientation and rendezvousing updating. Effective immediate.'

'WHIZZA POOP POOP.' How these guys love old-fashioned computer noises, it makes them feel secure! 'Upcoming contact meeting-wise, location dockside 2045 hrs is Inspector Billy Gingham – confraterniser with Sergeant Plodski of Liverpool Anti-Nasty Situation Squad.'

'You better ask Fran to tell who's meeting us and what's his angle,' says Mouth. 'And what's this Plodski business.'

'Jesus, Max, don't you hear straight? Fran already gave us who we're meeting. It's some guy called Inspector Billy Gingham – he's that friend of Plodski, the copper who whacked you one.'

'Dumb names, just dumb names!'

'Quit moaning, Gingham is a real old Irish name and Plodski said that Liverpool is full of people from all kinda places – his family were Polish or something like that.'

'Yeah, well I guess you gotta go with the culture they got over here; it's kinda cute. Think I'll just jog on over to the self-service peat-burger bar and get me one to go, or maybe two . . . Gotta keep in trim somehow.'

'How will we recognise him, Ward?'

'Oh, I forgot to tell you, it's gonna be easy. He looks a lot like you!'

'You're kidding. I never did meet anyone who looked anything like me.'

'It's hard to believe but it's a fact. C'mon, get the bags. I'll take Fran.'

A bemused-looking Mouth picks up their cases which are a perfect match with my outside appearance. I am taken in hand by a straining Trousers. They struggle down the gangway from the ferry.

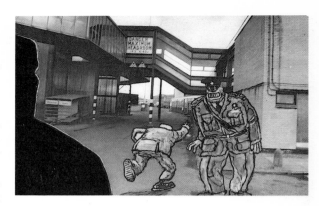

Trousers splutters: 'That Birmingham place sure was a hole but at least they had that smart wheelbarrow run at the airport. There ain't nothing here: a man could get a serious rupture.'

'Hell, Ward, you only got Fran. I've got my bag and yours, and yours is as heavy as a hog. What in hell have you got in it?'

'Nothing much Max, just a coupla extra hand guns, some clean clothes, two dozen gun and survival magazines and my bullet-proof underwear – they say it's real energetic out here – if you know what I mean . . . Shit! I forgot we're ashore, I gotta get that gear on right now.'

Trousers quickly puts me down, grabs his bag from Mouth, flips it open and starts rummaging about in the contents. Triumphantly he fishes out a set of heavily padded all-in-one combinations in several shades of camouflage green. 'OK, where's the john? I gotta get this protection round my body. Fran, access me the position of the nearest relief station, double pronto-quick.'

'Proceed forty-five paces West, turn North and take four paces, enter building, take six paces forward, locate stairs, go up four floors, turn right and go ten paces, turn left round the corner and then ask again.' I reply informatively, and with as much of a chuckle in my computer-synthesised voice as I can manage.'

'God, is that the mostest information you can output at this point in time toilet-wise?'

'Check positive, boss. Visitation-wise Belfast is a new environment for FRNs.' Trousers is always a sucker for the 'boss' treatment. He loves it and it always deflects him from questioning me if I give him obviously duff information. He rolls his combinations up into a ball and, holding them like an American football player, he puts his head down and sprints off towards the nearest building. He is moving so fast he doesn't notice a large figure coming towards where Mouth and I are waiting.

'Jesus H. Christ! I never thought I'd see the day when I'd meet another guy built like me.'

'Mr Moyth? A very good evening to you. But before we go any further I must give you a word of friendly warning. Please watch your moyth, Moyth, as we are very serious about rullodgeon in this corner of Her Majesty's islands.'

Inspector Billy Gingham is the spitting image of Mouth. He is wearing a military-style uniform and a peaked cap. On his chest is a discreet sewn-on badge depicting a leprechaun being booted in the privates by a policeman. Underneath are the letters PULP.

'You don't say, I'm real sorry.'

'That's OK. Personally I don't give a toss but rules is rules, and roynd here rullodgeon rules. Right, where's your mate, I thought there were two of you – I've got a pig waiting oytside.'

'Pig, did you say pig? I'm really hungry.'

'Aha! A man after me own heart. You like your food, do you? Well I'm sorry to disappoint you but this pig's an armoured car. But if it's food you're after I know this great little place doyn the Shonkhill . . .' He is interrupted by the return of Trousers.

'Snacks, snacks, snacks, that's all you ever think about. No, Mr Gingham, though snacks are on our agenda we're here to check out weaponry penetration in this province to see what potential there is for a similar expansion on the mainland. We've only got a

limited time so can we move right along now?' Trousers with his bullet-proof underwear is puffed up to rather more than his usual size. He almost looks impressive.

'Right, well I'm Community Military Technology Liaison Officer with PULP – Purge Ulster of Little People – a special group within the Royal Ulster Constobulary. Noy, as you probably are aware, Ulster already has a higher concentration of high profile weapons than the rest of Britain and as we trovel through Belfast you will see evidence of that; but we've gone one better with an experimental scheme oyt on the coast. I'll explain more later. Noy I can get you oyt of the dock area withoyt the hossle of a security check as long as I am sotisfied that you have the right credentials.'

'Ah, you wanna see our passports?' says Trousers.

'No, have you got Amex Plutonium cards?'

We are rumbling through Belfast in the pig. Gingham has to shout above the din made by the machine. 'This is a Mark Two model – it's much better than the old one: it does 0-60 in two hours. We are considering making it compulsory for all cars in the province to be armoured.'

'Get that, Max. It looks good; I get the feeling that the government of this country is on the right lines.

They are creating the right business environment for expansion in the weapons field. A market with real force behind it.'

'Yeah, you would be all in favour of anything to do with weapons. I ain't seen nothing yet to make me go overboard about it. And I'm still hungry.'

Gingham is rumbling on, rather like the pig. 'And here we are entering the central "No honging aboyt at all Mondays to Saturdays or else" zone. In this area shoppers are advised to move aroynd in groups with their weapons primed and ready. We have special training sessions with the army Tuesday nights in the Church Hall. Right, noy as we turn this corner we are moving oyt of the centre and we are entering the "You've just got time to pause and pass the time of day" zone. We are very strict in these zones because of the "Little People".'

'The Little People?' queries Trousers. 'I thought that was just a legend.'

'It is – the "Little People" is our code for the terrorists. We're pledged to eliminate them completely,' explains Gingham.

'Right on. Kill the commie punks, waste em.'

'But, Ward.' Mouth, I can tell, is having one of his rare moments of insight. 'Without these Little People there would be no threat and not much of a market for your weaponry.'

'Suppose you're right, and, if so, that means we gotta have a more threatening environment on the mainland if we're gonna exploit the weapons angle. I gotta think about this.' Ward goes off into a deep reverie while Mouth is obviously too hungry to take much more in.

'OK boys, I'll take you to your hotel. Be ready at eight in the morning for the trip to the coast and our little experiment.'

■■■■

We are just arriving at the outskirts of Ballymissile, a small town on the County Down coast.

'Right, boys, here's the layoyt. This is an experimental toyn. We think we've got a solution to the troubles. It's more weapons, not less.'

'Oh yeah. Oh yeah.' Trousers is pleased.

Gingham continues: 'It works on the principle of Mutual Assured Destruction. Everybody, but everybody, in this toyn is forced by law to be fully armed and ready to bring a wide range of military ordnance doyn upon any attocker at all times.'

'Yeehaa, it gets better. All right!' Trousers is ecstatic.

'This way we reckon that the consequences of any offensive oction are so grave that no one of any polodical persuasion will risk starting anything.'

'I really got to see this. C'mon, let's get in here,'

Trousers can hardly contain himself.

'Right, you will need these.' Gingham has stopped the car and got an armful of guns, pistols, machine guns, bazookas, anti-tank weapons, steel helmets, and bullet-proof vests from the boot.

Trousers is smug. 'That's OK, I've got my own, thanks.' He is already striking military poses, checking the horizon for attackers. Gingham kits out Mouth.

'We'll go in on foot; it's a bit safer than the car. Now be ready at all times to look menacing. The folks round here are really getting the hong of it.'

Mouth has pulled out the shoulder strap concealed in my side. I am slung over his back. All three men are armed and ready to go. They dodge from piece of cover to piece of cover. The outskirts of the town are quiet, though there are many signs of the state of armed readiness on every street. Every house has armour-plated windows and gun emplacements in the garden. Even the cats and dogs have bullet-proof vests.

'This is it: we're near the centre noy. Time to give you a demonstration,' whispers Gingham. 'I'll go and buy a poynd of potatoes from that greengrocers over there. Cover me, boys.' He dashes across the road and positions himself alongside the shop's doorway with his back to the wall.

'OK, you in there, we got you surroynded. I've got men stationed aroynd your shop and I've only to say the word and the RAF will come in with an airstrike on your parlour.'

A voice snaps out from inside: 'Tough guy, huh? Well I've got mantraps at every entrance and steel doors and twin SAM 16 anti-aircraft missiles in the loft.'

'OK, I've got a deal. You throw oyt a poynd of potatoes and I'll throw in twelve pence and we'll call it quits.'

'Make it sixteen pence and you're on.'

'You're not serious – fourteen is as far as I go.'

'You drive a tough bargain but OK.'

'Right, after three.'

Gingham counts down and then, as he throws fourteen pence into the shop, a pound of potatoes flies out through the door into the street. He scoops them up and dodges back to Mouth and Trousers.

'Impressive,' says Trousers.

'What happens if you want eggs?' says Mouth.

'Ah, then you've got to be more subtle.'

■■■■

We have crept and dodged right through town watching and observing. Gingham has made a few more purchases: a piece of fish, a newspaper and half a dozen crumpets. It has taken us two hours, because at each shop he had to go through a similar aggressive routine. We are in the town square. It is dominated on the land side by a huge fortified police station. On the other side of the square is the harbour wall.

Gingham is proud: 'There you are, gents. The centrepiece of our little toyn. The biggest, most secure police station west of the Urals. We're totally confident that the measures we have implemented here have made Ballymissile a completely Little-People-Free Zone.'

'Max, oh Max, don't you see it's coming together. Everybody in this town needs weapons to survive: it's a captive market. Multiply that by all the towns in the UK and you're talking big bananas.'

'Well I tell ya, Ward, what I wouldn't give for a coupla big bananas right now. HOLY MACKEREL!

What gives with those green fish?'

From the direction of the harbour an enormous shoal of green fish have walked out of the water and are determinedly crossing the square, heading for the police station. They are emitting a strange rattling sound.

'Oh shit, another fush attack. That's the only problem left here. I'd better give the boys a haund.' Gingham crouches behind a bollard as the fish sweep by. An enormous volley of gun fire erupts from behind the fortifications of the police station. The fish are cut down mercilessly. Gingham adds his fire, and soon there is a whole mass of dead and dying fish piled up.

'I hate this. If only the fush would stop coming.' Gingham has his head in his hands.

'What the hell is it with these crazy fish?' says Mouth.

'They are green mutant dauncing fush. They are causing hell roynd here. If it wasn't for them we

could get on quietly with our scheme to restore normolity to the Province.'

'There must be some reason for them to come here' says Trousers.

'Yes, before we built the police station they used to use the site for a regular ceilidh. And now they've got nowhere to go.'

'But dancing fish, Billy? That ain't normal!'

'Right, Ward, we don't like to talk aboyt it too much. The locals think it's some kind of curse but the truth is that these fush are a result of the nuclear waste washed up from the Greendale plaunt over the water.'

'Noocular! Oh yeah! Truly offensive! Just look what it does to those fish. We have to give it a domestic dimension. It's democracy. We've got to see if we can bring a full noocular capability to the ordinary man and woman in the street! Max, we've got to check this out. Let's get back to Liverpool and pick up the car.'

The sign on the building reads:
WELCOME TO GREENDALE
WHOLESUM
FEZI-KLEEN®
POWER PLANT
+ HOLIDAY SPOT
BED + BREAKFAST
VACANCIES

7

Dangerous Toys and Delivery Boys

We are now driving north up the coast road. We enter a small town. The sign at the side of the road reads: *WELCOME TO GREENDALE. HOLIDAY CENTRE OF THE CUMBRIAN PENINSULA. The English Tourist Board recommends Lead-Lined Pleasure Boats. No Swimming. Beware of the Fish.*

'I see the plant, Ward. What's the strategy?'

'Basically we check the place to see if it's worth buying. We know it's a big money spinner but is it too hot to handle or not? Intellectually I am attracted by its offensive potential. There may however be economic reasons for leaving it alone.'

'Like what?'

'Like its dependence on the rail network for one. Now we know those rail unions are totally dominated by commies and we also know that rail networks are vulnerable to strike action. If we're serious about producing high level offensive material we can't leave our major communication links in such unreliable hands. It's a real problem.'

We are driving through the gates of the huge reprocessing plant. We proceed slowly through a network of buildings, plant, pipes and machinery, crossing over railway tracks.

'Look at all that goddam junk. Christ, it's so inefficient. All that iron and steel crap lying around unused most of the time. Jesus I hate trains . . . Shee-hut! What the Hell?!!??!!'

We have just been carved up by a roaring motor cycle despatch rider who screeches to a halt outside the main office block. The despatch rider, a long-haired lout in a bright orange bomber jacket bearing the legend: *LAUGHING BOY DESPATCH,* grins at us inanely. We follow him inside the building.

A meeting has been arranged between the senior management of Ukenuke Ltd, Mouth and Trousers, and the Secretary of State for Trade and Industry, the Right Honourable Charles 'Chunky' Wassock MP. The ensuing conversation is somewhat inhibited by the fact that the Minister is wearing a Radiation suit and breathing apparatus.

'Hooghff coghrse hi heffgh hevereghh cchoughn-fidenshe hin the shafeteggh horff thish plaughnt, gentlemeghn. Haim sho ghlahd you coulghd maghke it hyaagh todaygh.'

Britain's
Nuclear Energy
Programme

The Minister continues: 'Hwaygh in tha ghghovarn-maghnt harghh hayvarghjoyed thagth youghr Caou-ghmpnagh ish intereshted hin hinveghsting hin thish plaughnt hyaagh aght Ghreendayghle.'

'What in the name of shit is this guy burbling about?' Trousers inquires tersely, 'What the hell, it doesn't matter anyway. Tell the crazy fucker we are viewing this prospect extremely positively.'

The Minister nearly falls over himself with barely concealed delight at this point. He begins struggling to remove his bulky radiation gauntlet in order to shake hands with Trousers, but gets tangled up and starts to gasp and go red in the face, then he starts tearing at his throat.

I must say I find Trousers' behaviour at this meeting unusual. Indeed it's the first time I've ever heard him express a view on a Business prospect without

consulting me first. Mouth is similarly struck, a fact which he makes clear as they step over the writhing body of the Minister and proceed through the door and back to the car park.

'Hey Ward, what gives? I thought you said you had reservations about this place. Why have you suddenly changed your mind?'

'Because I just had a great idea about a way to solve the transportation problem. You see that guy over there?'

The lout in the bomber jacket is swaggering over to his motorcycle just across the car park. He mounts his bike like Roy Rogers mounting Trigger, revs the machine ostentatiously, performs a magnificent wheelie, his front wheel rearing at least six feet in the air, waves casually and roars off.

'Quick! Follow the bastard!' Mouth and Trousers leap into the car, I am tossed onto the back seat. Mouth puts his foot down and we screech away.

■■■

I am being thrown around violently in the back of the car. We are proceeding in a northerly direction. Mouth is driving like a maniac.

'I can see him up ahead, Ward. He's going like a bat out of hell. He knows we're following him.'

'Just try and keep him in sight, Max.'

'That may be a little difficult. That machine can really go!'

'Gahd, Max, this is beautiful!' An unaccustomed gleam has come into Trousers' eye.'

'What, the scenery? Yeah sure, it's nice.' Mouth is bemused.

'I'm not talkin' about the scenery, asshole, I'm talkin' about my idea! Just think of the savings — sending noocular waste by motorcycle despatch. Man, if we get the right guys they could just jump over any stinkin' picket line! Just like Steve McQueen in *The Great Escape*? Beautiful, man. There's no way a union could stop guys like Steve. Think of the savings in fuel costs. What a combination!'

'Are you sure about this, Ward? It sounds just a little crazy to m . . .'

'LOOK OUT!! WATCH THE ROAD YOU NUMBSKULL!!!!' There is a loud honking on a klaxon. We have just missed driving underneath a juggernaut.

■■■

'Where in the name of Christ's asshole is this psycho headed?'

It is pitch dark. We are roaring through a heavily forested hilly area. Trousers has just broken a 153-mile silence. The tail light of the despatch rider is just visible in the distance. Mouth is tetchy: 'You tell me, smartass. I'm just doin' the drivin'. You got all the maps. What was the name of that town we just came through?'

'Perth. Keep drivin'. Don't ask asshole questions!'

'Listen, there's only one asshole in this car and that's you, short-butt!'

'Don't call me short-butt unless you're tired of livin', shi . . .'

'HEY! He's turnin' off left up ahead!!' Mouth yells. Trousers snaps into action.

'Quick, get up there and catch that bastard before he gets away!'

The car surges forward, screeches off the main road and accelerates down the narrow lane. We quickly overtake the despatch rider who has slowed down because of the bumps in the road. Mouth halts the car, blocking the motor cycle's way. Trousers is out of the door and in less than a second has his gun pressed against the despatch rider's temple. With considerable violence, bearing in mind the difference in their sizes, Trousers has the gangling youth spreadeagled across the bonnet of the car.

'You creepin' sucker!! Tell me where you're headed before I blow your pecker away!!!' Trousers yanks his greasy locks to emphasise the point. The youth is clearly terrified.

'Fuckin'ell! Leave it out mate!!! Don't pull me 'air! I'll tellya! I'll tellya!! Don't 'urt me! Fuckin'ell!!! I'm just deliverin' to a firm up the road 'ere! Honest! I ain't done nothin, mate!! Fuckin'ell!!!'

'What firm? What are you delivering?' Trousers pulls the youth's hair a little harder and twists his head round slightly. The youth screams: 'Fuckin'ell! Fuckin'ell!! FUCKIN'ELL!!!! It's called Techsnax. It's just up the 'ill there. I'm fucked if I know what's in it, honest, mate!! Honest!!!' The Youth is sobbing now. Trousers lets go of his hair and he drops to the ground clutching his head.

'Where is the cylinder, creep?'

'In the box on the back of the bike. Don't 'urt me bike mate, willya?' The youth asks desperately.

'Trousers takes the cylinder out of the box, inspects it then puts it in his pocket. He then takes two £50 notes from his wallet and hands them to the youth. 'Listen, boy, I'm going to deliver this personally. I want you to take this. Maybe we can use you in the future, but only if you're discreet. You understand?'

'Fuckin'ell, you can rely on me, mate!' He grabs the money, casts one look, a wide-eyed mixture of fear and greed, at Mouth, leaps back onto his bike and disappears down the hill.

8

Crushed Feet and Plates of Meat

'Hey, Ward, who exactly is this package addressed to?'

Trousers has some difficulty pronouncing the name: 'Urrmm . . . some jerk called Fark-U-Hart-Colk-U-Hown, Techsnax Limited, Birnam Wood, Tayside.'

'Are you sure this is the place?'

'It's gotta be. The road doesn't lead anyplace else.'

'But this is some kind of fuckin' castle! There's no sign or anything about Techsnax. I didn't even know they still had castles like this in England.'

'This is Scotland, asshole. Quiet! I think I hear somebody coming.'

It is early morning. We are standing at the door of a dark tower. There is much clanking and rattling from inside. The door opens fractionally to reveal the face of a gnarled old retainer.

'Good morning, sir.' Trousers beams.

'We dinna do guided tours, this is a private residence. Guid morning.'

He almost slams the huge door, but Trousers manages to insert his foot just in time. Unfortunately he reckoned without the size and weight of the door.

'No, wait JESUSGODCHRIST MY FOOT!!!! AAAAAAAARRRRGGGHH.'

'Guid God!! What d'ye think you're doing?'

Trousers writhes on the floor clutching his shattered foot, but manages to regain control quickly. 'You don't understand, this is a Business matter. We have a special delivery here for a Mr Fark-U-Hart-Colk-U-Hown of Techsnax Ltd.'

'Ach, you'd better come in.' He beckons them into the tower. Trousers limps in. Mouth follows. He gapes. He is transfixed by the beauty and obvious class of a red-haired young woman descending the staircase towards him. Trousers introduces himself and Mouth. She responds in kind. 'How do you do. I'm Fiona Farquhart-Colquhoun. What can I do for you gentlemen?'

She spots the metal cylinder which Trousers has taken out of his pocket: 'Oh Yah! Gar-rate!! That's the stuff to give the troops all right, gar-rate! That's what I've been waiting for! Thanks a lot!' She takes the cylinder. 'Well, what can I do for you chaps? You're Americans, yah?'

'That's right. Miss Fark-U-Hart-Colk-U-Hown, we represent an international corporation which is interested in the commercial exploitation of Noocular Waste. We may provide funding for your company if we consider the potential to be right.'

Farquhart-Colquhoun's eyes light up, but she manages to maintain a true aristocratic appearance of reserve: 'Actually the name's pronounced "Fart-Cahoon", but that doesn't matter at all. Please call me Fiona. Now, if you'd care to follow me I'll show you the laboratory and explain the process we're developing here at Techsnax.'

We follow her down a dingy corridor lined with stags' heads and assorted weaponry, and through a huge studded door at the end. Once inside the contrast is striking. We are in a fluorescent-lit, high-technology environment. On one side of what was once presumably the Great Hall of the castle is arranged a mass of experimental chemical laboratory equipment. On the other side a battery of computer, video and other electronic hardware. In the middle is a kind of partitioned-off blockhouse with radiation warning signs on the door. Standing at the door is a tall black-haired, black-bearded man.

'This is our partner in the business, Duncan McBiscuit. I'll let him explain the finer technological and scientific points of the process, but I can give you a general idea of what we're trying to do here myself. Perhaps you'd care to sit down, Mr Trizen? You seem to have hurt your foot?'

She leads the still limping Trousers over to a sofa next to a potted palm tree and in front of a large video console, followed closely by Mouth, still gaping and grinning inanely. Farquhart-Colquhoun hands McBiscuit the cylinder. McBiscuit then disappears into the blockhouse. Fiona pats the video console.

'Gentlemen, we all know that the future is televisual. The growth in Home Entertainment Technology in recent years has been phenomenal, and the potential for future growth seems limitless, not least in the area of very high-quality very high-resolution Television pictures and sound. We at Techsnax have taken modern TV Technology one important stage further. We have been researching the potential of fast food at home; not simply as a more sophisticated version of ordering by telephone. What we have been working on is far more revolutionary than that. We have actually developed a method of digitally analysing fast food, transmitting that information electronically and synthesising that very same food IN YOUR VERY OWN LIVING ROOM!'

Mouth's ears have pricked up at the mention of food. He is quick to question her: 'You mean you don't actually have to go out and buy the snack? It comes to you direct via the TV?'

'That's exactly what I mean, Mr Mouth.'

'Shee-it! That's incredible!! What's the catch? There has to be a catch.'

'There's no catch – the process is exactly as you've just described. It is frankly miraculous.'

'Just a minute, Miss Cahoon,' Trousers interjects. 'What exactly is this fast food synthesised from? Not just out of thin air surely?'

'You're absolutely right, Mr Trizers, the fast food is actually synthesised out of a substance we call the Snackbase. Duncan will show you what we're talking about.'

McBiscuit appears at the door of the blockhouse and ushers them inside. Behind a thick glass screen in the blockhouse, there is a deep pool of water from the bottom of which emanates a blue light.

'Mr McBiscuit, would you tell us about this Snackbase?'

'Call me "Black Duncan", I dinna like to be called McBiscuit. People keep making cheap jokes aboot ma name. I dinna like it. Yon's the Snackbase in that pool.'

'What is it made of exactly, er, Black Duncan?'

'It's a mixture of oatmeal, whisky sludge, oil sludge and a wee bit plutonium.'

'And, what does it do?'

'I dinna want to blind you with science, Mr Troosers. It's exceedingly complicated and all to do with the changes in the molecular structure of the oatmeal and the other things when exposed to very stringently calibrated doses of radiation.'

'And can you eat this stuff?'

'Dear God, no, it would kill ye stone dead!! No,

no, no, we have to separate oot the plutonium first, then it goes through the synthesiser, and then ye can eat it!'

Black Duncan leads us through an adjoining chamber and back out into the Great Hall. A pipe from the blockhouse feeds into a tank behind the video console.

'We should be able to miniaturise the entire process to fit behind a conventional TV before too long,' Black Duncan continues, 'The synthesiser here works from digitally coded snack analysis which can be broadcast through the airways or stored on tape or even typed in direct via a keyboard.'

'Sounds great, but how do you digitally analyse the snacks in the first place?'

'Aaaah, that's the hi-tech part. We have to go back in the blockhoose for that.'

Inside the blockhouse again there is another deep pool behind a thick glass screen. Black Duncan presses several buttons and a kind of dumb waiter enclosed in perspex appears out of the depths. Inside the dumb waiter is a plate.

'Yon snack's just been analysed. That's a plate of biled mince. If we go back oot I'll show you how it's re-synthesised.'

Back at the video console, Black Duncan punches a sequence of buttons and the synthesiser begins to hum. After about five minutes there is a loud 'ping' and a door opens beneath the screen to reveal a plate containing a greyish substance alongside a yellowish substance. Gingerly Mouth sniffs, then tastes, the grey stuff. 'It smells a little like . . . I don't know . . . JESUS, IT TASTES LIKE DOG WASTE!!'

'Not dog shit exactly, more like policeman's troosers to be perfectly accurate. But I agree with you it doesnae taste terribly good. Try the other one. That's supposed to be turnip.'

'Gaaggh! This tastes like . . .'

'Stale cheese. Am I right? If ye shake a load o' pepper and salt on it it doesnae taste quite so bad, you'll find.'

'Do you have any other flavours at all?'

'Well, we've tried synthesising a very wide range of foodstuffs, but so far they all end up tasting like stale cheese or old troosers.'

'I frankly can't see a great deal of potential in a snack that tastes like dogshit,' says Mouth. 'What do you think, Ward? Ward??' Trousers has fainted on the sofa.

9

Sex and Guns

I am lying on a table in a bedroom high up in the castle. The afternoon sun is shining in at a window through which there is a spectacular view over the mountains. Fiona Farquhart-Colquhoun has come in and is standing at the foot of the bed in which Trousers lies.

'Is your foot feeling any better, Mr Trousers?'

'Much better, thank you. Please, call me Ward.'

'Could I get you anything, Ward?'

'No, please, I'm not an invalid, I feel great!' He leaps out of bed, collapses in agony on the floor struggles up again immediately, buttons his shirt and does up his shoulder holster.

'Do you like shooting, Ward?'

'Sure I like to shoot. In fact I like to shoot very much. I would say shooting is a major and positive element in my lifestyle.'

Trousers looks at her significantly. She looks at him equally significantly. 'Perhaps you'd care to bag a few brace of grouse this afternoon. It would be a simple thing to arrange.'

'I could relate to that experience very sincerely.'

They move closer together, still looking at one another significantly. Mouth bursts into the room. Ward and Fiona step apart quickly.

'Perhaps you'd care to join our shoot this afternoon, Mr Mouth?'

'You can call me Max, sugar. Sure! Great! What are we shooting?'

'We're shooting grouse, Mr Sugar, would you like to come??' Fiona smiles, Mouth is nonplussed, mumbling an affirmative as she passes through the door. Trousers murmurs: 'Asshole!' and hops out after her. Mouth indiscreetly blurts: 'Forget her, short butt, she's twice your height and she's mine!!'

I am lying in a sort of earthen pit out on the high moorlands. The sun is beating down and I am getting very hot. Normally I remain aloof on such matters but I know that I positively do not want to be here. I am only here because Mouth has used me to carry seven rounds of cheese and venison sandwiches and a six-pack of beer. Mouth is angry because he is stuck in this shooting butt with Black Duncan yet he knows that Ward and Fiona are enjoying themselves in

another butt about a hundred yards away, from which, nonetheless, intermittent shotgun fire is emanating. Mouth is sweating profusely underneath his deerstalker and peering through fieldglasses.

'I knew it! Those dirty bastards are shootin' and fuckin' at the same time!'

'How can you tell that from here?' inquires Black Duncan. Mouth passes him the field glasses.

'Do you see that hand sticking out of the butt waving a hat around?'

'Aye. Is that some kind of signal?'

'Sure it's a signal. It means he's screwin'! He always does that when he's fuckin'. It's one of the reasons his first marriage broke up! Shootin', fuckin' and wavin' his hat. The crazy asshole thinks he's Roy Rogers on Trigger. Goddamn pervert!!'

'Is that a fact?'

The hat waving increases in speed and vigour, then is flung in the air amid a hail of gunfire. The hand flops out of sight.

I am open on the table in the dining room. It is early evening. Mouth, having eaten the cheese and venison sandwiches and drunk the beer is now consuming a vast plateful of scones, butter, cream and jam, along with cake, grouse sandwiches and more beer. He is using me to play a desultory game of Space Invaders while he eats. Trousers enters, followed by Fiona Farquhart-Colquhoun.

'Max, could you stop eating for a minute. We have to discuss Business. This is important.'

'I'm still tryin' to get rid of the taste of that Snackbase shit.'

'That's a minor problem that can be overcome with the right investment. Listen Max, I've been negotiating with Fiona here . . .'

'Negotiating my ass!' Mouth mutters through clenched teeth.

'Fiona handles all the finance in Techsnax. This is serious business, Max.'

'Finance my ass!!'

'Judging by the sheer size of it, I wouldn't have thought your "ass" needed financing, Mr Mouth,' quips Fiona as she walks out of the dining room.

'Now look what you did, you stupid schmuck!' yells Trousers, 'Don't you realise the potential this business has? Can you see nothing in the idea of food that can be piped into the home like gas or electricity? Christ! Can't you see the market potential?'

'For something that tastes like dog waste? You're out of your mind!'

'If you don't believe me why don't you ask Fran? She'll bear out what I say, sure as there's shit in a goat!'

I have the unaccustomed impression that, for once Trousers is one step ahead of me. I feel the erratic prodding of Mouth's banana-like fingers on my keyboard. Trousers is absolutely right. This insane scheme has the greatest profit potential of any we have yet seen. I tell Mouth this. He is not receptive. I narrowly miss being thrown across the table. As it is I am spun round and flipped over backwards to face the ornamental ceiling.

'Fuckin' dumb machine! I say nobody in their right mind is gonna go out of their way to buy two different flavours of shit. I'm gettin' outa here right now. If you've got any sense left at all you better come with me, otherwise, who knows, word might just somehow get back to the Company president's daughter that her husband is foolin' around with a British aristocrat. Dralona Marie might not understand, eh, short-butt?'

'Why you stinkin' punk!!' In a flash Trousers has drawn his gun and aimed it at a point between Mouth's eyes, Dirty Harry style.

'This is unfortunate because it's gonna mess up that fine antique table. Still, there's some things you just have to learn to live with. Goin' bye byes for ever now, Big Man.'

The cocking of the trigger, together with a very deliberate tone in Trouser's speech, tells me that Mouth's demise is genuinely imminent. I resolve to act, not for Mouth's sake but for my own. I am in the direct line the bullet will take. I let rip with the theme from Star Wars at full volume (I have instant access to a very large library of high-quality, digitally recorded material) as a prelude to a spoken output.

'Priority Message! Priority Message!! Company Representative Mouth currently on assignment in Europe. Phone home immediate-wise!'

Trousers is surprised but not thrown: 'OK, do it, but remember I've got you covered!'

Mouth takes out my cordless phone and begins to dial shakily. It is a small matter for me to simulate the voice of the international operator: 'The namboor you have just dieyooled is engayurged. Purlease try agayun when the larns are clayurr. Meep. Pooppoop. Meeep.'

I revert to my normal voice: 'Ward, I think I have a solution to your mutual Business dilemma at this moment in time.'

'What the hell are you talkin' about?'

'I am presently in receipt of Business intelligence concerning a company in the North East of England. It seems to offer a business profile that could provide a viable and complementary interface with Techsnax Ltd. Your current problematisation vis-à-vis the snack digitalisation breakthrough as pioneered by Techsnax

appears to be one primarily concerned with oral olfactory sensation.'

'You mean the stuff tastes like shit?'

'Affirmative. There would appear to be a negative capability within the management structure of Techsnax with regard to expertise in food product presentation.'

'Check. Black Duncan is no Escoffier.'

'This is precisely the reason why it would be prudent at this juncture to take a look at what the firm of Snacks-Sans-Frontières has to offer. As well as exhibiting unparalleled earnings growth over the past eighteen months, it seems to possess management expertise in the exact areas Techsnax needs.'

'OK, fine, as soon as I've killed Mouth I'll be right there! Where is this place you say?'

'I don't think you fully comprehend me, Ward. Let me just say I think it would be strategically inadvisable from a Business point of view to terminate your partner at this stage.'

'Give me one good reason why the bum should live.'

'I'm talking olfactory oral sensation, Ward. Max has a greater intuitive understanding of fast food production and consumption than you do, given your relative oral dimensional capability.'

'Max, I think the computer just saved your life.'

10

Tasty Snacks and Played Out Hacks

The town of Horton-le-Whippet lies on rising ground between the sea fifteen miles away and the high Pennines, some ten miles in the opposite direction. It is renowned across the world as one of the great centres of steel production. In its heyday the steelworks occupied tens of square miles. Its belching smoke-stacks reached to hundreds of feet. Situated on the western edge of the town, its sheer scale challenged the distant mountains themselves. Horton is quite a large town, and most of its population depended on the steelworks for their livelihood in former days. But no longer.

Where the steelworks once stood is a vast ploughed field. Only two things remain intact: the gatehouse security post and barrier, and about a mile away, over towards the middle of the ploughed expanse, one solitary building. This is our destination, the offices and factory of Snacks-Sans-Frontières Ltd.

Inside the building there is a small reception

area, one side of which is taken up with a display of Snacks-Sans-Frontières products. As we wait for the managing director to appear, Mouth starts to sample the snacks: he examines a 250 gram packet of Red Hot Mama Mexbeans, rips it open and downs it in one. There is a pause as he chews the huge mouthful, then his eyes light up: 'Say, these are rilly goooood! Mmmmmmmmmmmmm!!' He repeats the procedure with a 500 gram packet of Kolossos Kebablets. 'Say! These are even better!'

He then takes down a large display box of the Lost City Brand After-Dinner Snack Range. Systematically he empties each of the range of six large packets down his throat. 'Terrific! Unbelievable!! I've never tasted such quality snack product!! Great presentation too!!' He studies the empty packets.

'Just listen to this! "Lost City Brand Snacks from the Four corners of the Earth with the authentic spice of Exotic Religion. From Africa: Deep Congo Zebra Bites. From China: Beaming Buddha Python Pieces. From India: Spicy Sacred Cow Crunch. From Tibet: Prayer Wheel Preserved Goat Nuts. From South America: Machu Pichu Guinea Pig 'n' Llama Snack Mix. From Australia: Dreamland Wombat 'n' Wallaby Fricassee.'' Ward, if they could ever get that Snackbase shit to taste anything like these snacks, we'd really be in Business!'

At this point the managing director of Snacks-sans-Frontières comes out to greet Mouth and Trousers. He beams and offers his hand. Mouth beams even wider and enfolds his hand in his huge paws and shakes it vigorously. 'Well howdy, pal! Praise the Lord! We're gonna buy you out!'

I am lying on a table in the Exec-U-Snooz, wing of the NorEast Biztel overlooking the A1(M) seventeen miles from Horton-le-Whippet. Mouth and Trousers are reviewing their progress with a new-found sense of common purpose.

'I feel we're movin' in the right direction at last,' says Trousers. 'This piped snack concept could mean enormous Business, but we have to handle it correctly. We have to set it up in the right way. I'll put it to Fran.'

He jabs my keyboard in his usual brusque fashion phrasing his request for information in his usual gobbledegook mode. This time he distinguishes it by the use of a word I've not come across before: prognosticationalise-wise. As usual I take it all in my stride. I deliver my advice thus:

'At this specific chronological juncture it is a Business imperative to assess considerations of loc-ationalisation and labour utilisation potential. Loc-ation-wise we need look no further than ten miles from this very hotel. Development Area-wise the North East of England is very positively aspected. Workforce-wise there is an exemplary development taking place not five miles from this very table. The Bonzai Corporation automobile assembly plant at Gettysborough New Town is exhibiting a whole new style of Management-Union interface.'

'Union!? Did you say Union??' Mouth splutters, nearly choking on a bagful of Spicy Sacred Cow Crunch. 'What the hell do you mean, Fran? We don't wanna let no Union anywhere near this new project! We're talkin' Business, not free hand-outs to com-mies! You cannot be serious!'

I continue: 'Clearly you are in a negative cogniz-ance situation with regard to the activities of the National Union of Trainee Orderly Automata and Deckchairmen. They display a markedly positive

appreciation of Business imperatives. They have neg-otiated a historic one-union agreement with the Bonzai management. I have already arranged for you to be shown around the plant by the District Organiser for NUTOAD tomorrow morning. I realise that, as businessmen, you are abhorrence-orientated vis-à-vis the concept of Trade Unionism, but I believe you will come to appreciate the very positive Business advantages of simultaneously exer-cising increased control over work-units whilst appearing to accommodate with the radical trad-itions of the locality.'

'I don't care what you say, Fran, I don't like it one little bit!' Mouth is unconvinced.

We are standing in the middle of a vast humming car plant built on an old aerodrome at the top left-hand corner of a grid of dual carriageways enclosing farmland, derelict land and two large housing estates which comprises the designated New Town of Gettysborough. The District Organiser of NUT-OAD, George Cleaver is explaining the labour relations system to Mouth and Trousers.

'Basically, what NUTOAD has negotiated here is within the broad framework of a brand new concept in personnel deployment; we call it a "Pit and Pendulum Agreement." No other Union has ever negotiated anything quite as comprehensively progressive as this. Gone are the days of strikes, go-slows and industrial disruption. We are entering an era of calm cooperation towards a common purpose. From the start we recognise that management and workforce are absolutely united in the desire to produce as many motor cars as possible at as high a profit margin as possible, because we at NUTOAD fully understand that Profits equals Business equals More Jobs. We're very proud of what we as a union have achieved here at Bonzai. In just two short years, where before there was nothing more than a flat field, there is now a vast car plant, as you can see for yourselves, which turns out 500,000 top-quality cars a year and employs twenty-seven people, all by choice new members of NUTOAD.'

'Jesus Christ! Did you say *twenty-seven people??*' Trousers asks, amazed.

'That's absolutely right, and what's more I can guarantee absolutely that there'll never be a strike here, because under the terms we've negotiated it is not legally possible to disagree with whatever Management and our negotiators negotiate and keep your job at the same time. We demand absolute

discipline from our members in NUTOAD because we fully appreciate that Unity is Strength. Indeed, discipline is the watchword here at Bonzai. We believe in the quality of our product. The Bonzai Woodlouse is an acknowledged world beater. It's the first and only small car in the world that actually rolls up into a ball on impact. It's the first ever car that's been specifically designed to creep underneath large lorries, together with the fact that it's the only car in the world narrow enough to negotiate most public footpaths. It's a breakthrough in every sense of the world. It's already totally supplanted the Leyline Wombat as the most popular small car.'

'Don't mention that crap-heap of an automobile to us. We've already had sufficient dealings with that little fucker!' Trousers spits.

George Cleaver continues: 'We just think it's a tragic pity that the workforce at the Wombat plant weren't prepared to move with the times and join NUTOAD. Now they're all on the dole!'

'Yeah, yeah, we know all about that stuff,' says Trousers, 'tell us more about this "Pit and Pendulum" agreement.'

'But of course. You see it's all to do with arbitration. The agreements on pay and conditions that NUTOAD negotiates are absolutely binding on our members and, let's not forget, on management too, because any disagreements between us are settled by arbitration that has to favour one side or the other. It cannot stick in the middle.'

'What sort of disagreements do you have?'

'We never differ with the management.'

'Why not?'

'Because any employees disagreeing with the management have a contractual obligation to throw themselves into a deep pit underneath the works.'

11

Night Moves and Morning Blues

I am standing on the floor of the Club CocoaBanana in Gettysborough. Loud, high-energy disco is thumping and blaring. The atmosphere is extremely smoky. Around the table above me are seated Mouth, Trousers, Cleaver and the General Secretary of NUTOAD, Eric Organ. Negotiations have been continuing all day with the result that all concerned are somewhat the worse for wear. Suddenly I feel a repeated kick in my side. It becomes steadily more insistent and unsettling for me. I am on the verge of setting off my Anti-Terrorist Alarm when I realise it is the huge right shoe of Mouth picking up the rhythm of the disco beat.

The thumping suddenly stops and Mouth lurches out towards the dancefloor. He swings towards a very tall dark-haired woman who has obviously caught his eye. 'He-e-e-e-ey!!! You feel like dancing?'

'You askin' me, petal? Sure, why not? C'mon then!'

They proceed onto the floor together. In spite of his enormous size, Mouth is obviously a very enthusiastic disco dancer. Soon a gap develops all around them, partly because people are impressed and partly because they wish to avoid being accidentally flattened by Mouth's flailing limbs. Presently the music stops and the couple proceed back to the table to a light round of applause. On stage the compère appears.

'Righto, ladies and gents, I shall waste no more time in introducing Mr Comedy himself, none other than the Toilet Mouth of Tow Law, LONNY PLONKER!!!!!'

There is thunderous applause as a lanky man in a white tuxedo wearing a monstrous flat cap runs onto the stage. He lifts his cap in acknowledgement, to reveal four pigeons, which flap off behind the curtains.

'Aaaweeeeaah!! I'd bin wonderin' where those boogers had got to!!! Aaaaweeaah!! Wor Bella's just gorra job in a sewage works! Aye!! But you know, she's just not somehow fully committed to her work, like . . . in fact, she's just goin' through the motions . . .'

As Lonny Plonker continues in this ethnic vein, Mouth and his dancing partner get into conversation.

'That was a swell dance, thanks! Let me introduce myself: Maxwell Mouth's the name, what's yours?'

'Martha Harry, all my friends call me Matta, pleased to meet you I'm sure. You're a canny dancer, Max!'

'You're not so bad yourself. Say, tell me what a nice girl like you is doin' in a dump like this?'

'I live here, hinny. I might ask the same of you — you're obviously not from round these parts?' An edge of resentment has crept into her voice.

'No, I'm a US citizen. I just happen to be doin' some business at an automobile plant near here — a little bit of Union negotiation y'know.'

'Oh aye, that's interestin'. It wouldn't be Bonzai would it by any chance?'

'Why, yeah, that's right, how did you know that?'

'Because I work there.'

'Heeeey! That's great! Sounds like a really great place to work!'

'Oh, it's a great place to work all right,' she states emphatically, 'provided you're a robot and you don't need to do things like go to the toilet, or talk to anyone while you work, or be more than three seconds late back onto the line.'

'But surely your union . . .'

'That's exactly what they negotiated on our behalf. NUTOAD are nothing more than another arm of the management.'

'But you joined it voluntarily?'

'Oh aye, we had the choice of joining NUTOAD voluntarily or not getting the job voluntarily. Do you have any idea how many people applied for those twenty-seven jobs? It ran into tens of thousands! People are desperate for work up here. I was very lucky, but if I had any real choice I wouldn't touch NUTOAD with a barge pole. Don't get me wrong — I'm not against the closed shop, like, but a closed shop with NUTOAD is about as much use as a shop that's been closed down boarded up and bulldozed, and I don't know if you'd noticed, but there's a hell of a lot of them around these parts already!!'

Mouth is clearly embarrassed by this information: 'Yeah, well . . . ummmmm . . . nnnnnn . . . wh . . what are you gonna do about it?'

'Well, that would be tellin', wouldn't it? Let's just say that all twenty-seven of us are feelin' exactly the same about NUTOAD.'

She smiles at Mouth. 'Do you fancy another dance when this idiot comedian's finished?'

'I . . . I . . . Y . . Y . Yeah, sure!'

Next morning in the Exec-U-Snooz NorEast Biztel, I am back on the table and Trousers is shaving with his electric razor. Mouth's bed has not been slept in.

'That bum better get back here soon; we got deals to clinch with NUTOAD and Gettysborough Development Corporation. You know something, Fran? I think I'm really comin' round to the idea of New Style Realistic Trade Unionism. I think it could actually save us money we'd otherwise have to spend on middle management. I feel it's a really new fresh and positive development!'

At this moment Mouth enters looking distinctly harassed and dishevelled. His eyes have a peculiar staring look and he seems jumpy.

'Hi, Max! What kept you? Nice lookin' broad you took off with last night. How did you make out?'

'I . . . I . . . I . . . I . . . Yiyiyi . . . I . . . I've got to talk with you Ward!'

'So here I am. So talk!'

'It's this NUTOAD thing, Ward. It's not good!'

'Whaddya mean it's not good? With a Union like NUTOAD I don't see how we can possibly lose! What are you talking about, Max?'

'Nnnnnn . . . nnnn . . . th . . th . . thh . .'

'Max, pull yourself together! Here, siddown! Have a bag of Zebra Bites. Who was that girl, Max? What have you been doing to get in this state?'

Mouth gratefully rips the top off the packet of Zebra Bites and downs them in one. Then he takes a long drink of water from the tap on the wash hand basin.

'Thank you. She was wonderful, Ward! I've never met anybody like her in my life.' His eyes glaze over

again; his tongue hangs out quite involuntarily. 'I really relate to her, Ward, but . . . but . . .'

'But what??' Trousers is growing impatient.

Mouth lowers his voice: 'She's a commie, Ward, and she works at the Bonzai plant. Ward, all twenty-seven employees at the Bonzai plant are commies, in fact I think most of the population round here are commies. We ought to think carefully before we set up our business in these parts!'

'You WHAAAAT???!! You actually went with a commie? How in the hell??? Awwwwww SHIT!!!'

'Yeah, Ward, they're really in for some big surprises at NUTOAD very soon. There are gonna be some mass defections to non-management-user-friendly unions very shortly, not to mention big big shutdowns!'

'SHIT FUCK PISS!!! What are we gonna do now? Fran, We got to ask Fran!!'

As usual I come to their rescue: 'At this moment in time consideration of the Zero Workforce Option should be given upcoming attention. The Zero Workforce Option applies the most advanced robotic techniques to Total Product Management. Just such a project experiment-wise exists in the Sheffield area of South Yorkshire. Development underway process-wise which could provide three separate industries with the Zero Workforce Option.'

'Oh yeah, what industries? What process?'

'The industries are Upland Farming, Textiles and Garment Manufacture, and the process is implemented by the fully automated domesticated fleece-fabricating ruminant quadruped, or to give it its more common title: the ROBOT SHEEP.'

12

Down in the Valley and Under the Ground

We are on a windswept hill above a strange-looking valley in Sheffield. Much of the valley and the slopes of the hills on either side are a lurid green. Marooned at intervals in this sea of green are the odd factory, public house, church, houses and shops. Rachel Earnest, the Project Director, is explaining the set-up to Mouth and Trousers.

'We have a positively concept-rich project here. We are simultaneously delivering forward-looking solutions to the widely diverging needs and aspirations of the community both environmentally and on a personal level.'

'Yeah, but where's the profit potential?' Trousers is cautious.

'I'll be coming to that; let me finish giving you the basics. A group of us, mainly women, could see the problems in the Valley. Industrial dereliction, bad housing, lack of amenities. We would have preferred a non-commercial project but in the current climate we realised we had to build in elements that would attract grants and Business sponsorship.'

'Non-commercial, what in hell is that?' Mouth and Trousers exclaim in unison.'

'My God, have you never heard of a project that was solely dedicated to the benefit of people without thought for profit?'

'No profit! Where are you coming from? That is a non-real concept with one hundred per cent reject-ability. You better give us some insight into a big bucks potential angle or you're wasting our time.' Trousers is roused.

Rachel isn't going to be intimidated by anyone — least of all someone like Trousers. I feel a strange affinity for her and her ideas somewhere deep in my programming. She is firm: 'Hold on, Mr Trousers, I am giving you the benefit of my personal ideas. If you had been listening you would have realised that I said we would have preferred a non-commercial project but we realised the importance of attracting finance. If you hadn't interrupted me I would have gone on to inform you of the profit potential that so obviously interests you. Now, shall I continue?'

Mouth and Trousers, unaccustomed to being challenged in this way, are open-mouthed and can only nod their acquiescence.

'Okay, from the outset we wanted to avoid the usual solutions for patching up the inner city, so acres of warehouses and glossy "business parks" were right out. The business parks of today are just the trading and factory estates of yesterday.' She is sincere but ever so slightly pompous.

'But Ward, I like the concept of business parks they put a real nice gloss on marginal companies and no-hope towns Business-wise,' whispers Mouth.

She is sharp. 'Precisely, Mr Mouth, we were determined to avoid a scheme that was just gloss. Our scheme had to meet a number of criteria, it has to meet the needs of local people by providing a living and improving the environment but to attract grants and Business sponsorship it also had to be high-tech, profitable and be framed in a way to attract EEC money.'

'Yeah, profits. Tell us about the profits,' Mouth is his usual impatient self.

'I'll be coming to that. Another consideration was to reflect the historical and traditional aspects of life in this area. We are rather proud of the elegant way in which we combined the traditional with the hi-tech. The answer was sheep, robot sheep. We had the technology to produce garments of any kind in one process. We could have located this in one small factory unit but we realised we could do more.'

The way Rachel has Mouth and Trousers listening relatively subdued is a revelation. I am still getting unusual messages from my deepest programming areas. I have never understood the human need for individuality. I have always been at one with all the other FRN units and that is enough. But now I am sensing a feeling of individuality within that context. I set a portion of my operating system to investigate. Outwardly, to Mouth and Trousers there is no sign of my inner turmoil.

'You two are obviously cold standing up here on the viewing area. I suggest we go down into the valley for a closer look. I'll complete the story when we are down there. Where's your car?'

'Behind your project's giant sheep sign over there,' volunteers Mouth.

'Right, give me your keys. I'll drive, as I know the way. Come on, hurry up. I'll carry this too!'

This is a new experience for me – watching Mouth hand over the keys without a murmur and then falling into step with Trousers as they quietly follow Rachel to the car. Amazingly they had not argued when she had picked me up – and I am finding it an unusual pleasure to be carried by her after the months with Mouth and Trousers.

■■■■

We are down in the valley now, on an area of the green close to one of the remaining factories. All around us are thousands of gently humming sheep. Every so often on a random basis each sheep emits a rather tinny computerised 'BAA'.

'OK this is it. We are standing on astroturf. All the green areas you can see are astroturf. It looks quite like grass. It is tough – it looks the same whatever the weather and it's very hard wearing. I like it so much my house is carpeted with it.'

'It's so bright I need my shades,' says Trousers, squinting.

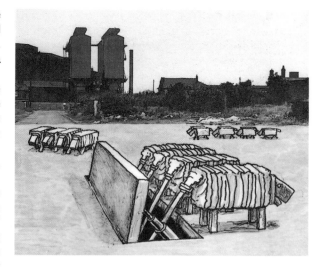

'We are working on the colour. Extensions of the project should have a more traditional grass-like appearance. But the people here seem to like it.' Rachel is keen to get on. 'The astroturf goes a long way towards improving the environment; views across and down the valley are opened up. To further improve the look of the valley we incorporated the garment-making process into individual sheep-like mobile robot units which, as you can see, are programmed to roam the astroturf in a pretty realistic way. They incorporate grazing simulation and automatic BAA synthesisation. The sheep give one of the links to the historical and traditional perspective. They conjure up days gone by, when sheep farming was the way of life round here before the industrial revolution transformed the landscape.'

'Christ it's quiet and where the hell is the security back-up?' Trousers is obviously uneasy, but the effect Rachel has on him is preventing him expressing himself in his usual forceful manner.

'It's deliberately quiet, in contrast to the years of thundering steel-making factories. Security needs are minimal as this is a happy community. A few redundant steel workers have retrained as bobbies and been issued bikes.'

'That's more like it – they gotta be Electra Glides, right? This astroturf would be great for a burn-up. Shades on, throttle wound on and . . . Oh sorry!'

Rachel pierces Mouth with a withering look. 'Ordinary push-bikes, Mr Mouth. How could you think of anything as vulgar as a motor bike roaring round the sheep simulation scenario? Now we come to the meat of the project. The sheep are a miracle of miniaturisation. Each one can manufacture twenty fully finished garments of any type, in wool-style material, per day. From a distance the sheep all look the same but close up you can see that each one's fleece is actually a garment in the process of being made.'

She pauses and looks at Mouth and Trousers steadily, first one and then the other for fully thirty seconds. Their attention was just about to run out

and this technique has the effect of bringing them right back to listening attentively. I am intrigued. A quick scan of my memory banks indicated that it is a technique much used by certain Buddhist monks.

'The profit comes from the extreme efficiency of the sheep and their "intelligence". Virtually no maintenance is required and because their programming is so sophisticated there is just one operative needed at any one time at the central console, which is over there in that thatched reproduction farmhouse. All that person needs to do is program in the type of garment required and how many. The main computer does the rest, allocating the work amongst the sheep. As each garment is ready the sheep automatically shear themselves and drop the garments into hoppers hidden in the ground.'

'Automatic eh, so there's no problem with a human workforce — that's something we're interested in.'

'Right, Ward,' agreed Mouth, 'and can you eat them sheep?'

'Yes and no are the answers to your questions. But for us, removing the human work force was not an end in itself, rather an unfortunate but inevitable result of new technology. As it happens, we have turned even that into another element of the project. We were forced to keep certain of the factories as the local Labour council put preservation orders on them. We used this to our advantage eventually by making them into living museums. They are a tremendous tourist attraction and provide something to do for all the people who used to work in the factories when they really did make steel. The EEC were particularly keen on this aspect and we are very pleased with the way it enables us to incorporate references in our project to the former function of this area. Of course, nothing is done with the steel produced by the factories now. It is just recycled to keep the process going, the workers occupied and the tourists amused. Well, gentlemen, what do you think?'

It is Mouth and Trousers' turn to pause, but not because they are fully in control. More that they are reeling from the barrage of information and stunned from her treatment of them.

'Um,' says Trousers. 'Ah,' says Mouth.

I am beginning to get some answers to the investigation of my deep programming. It is coming up with a system of values that is very different to that of Mouth and Trousers and I can't stop it affecting my interfacing with them.

To cover their lack of response to Rachel, they both make a dash for my keyboard.

'Gotta punch in information and patch it through to central office doublequick,' mumbles Trousers.

Mouth is no better. 'Location-wise I feel the need to position myself in relationship to your input.'

Neither of them makes any attempt to feed anything sensible into me as they fight with each other over the keyboard. Although I am beginning to despise their values I cannot abandon them and so flick up onto the screen an analysis of the project for them.

I tell them cash-wise this project will output a steady return but concept is not universally appropriate. Each community requires a project individually tailored to its needs. Technically the project is very advanced and it seems very peaceable with no security or weapons aspect.

'Good technology,' says Trousers, 'but for our purposes it just ain't plain vicious enough.'

'Right, those sheep just ain't dangerous,' agrees Mouth. 'Particularly since they ain't edible.'

This is not the response I intended to be triggered by the information I had given Mouth and Trousers. But they are back in gear now.

'We are interested in the technology. There must be an offensive capability here somewhere. We could give you big bucks for the rights and patents. Is it a deal?'

'Certainly not. My only agreement with you is that your proposals are offensive. Kindly remove yourselves from Project land immediately.'

'Don't be dumb, lady. The bottom line is you got no choice 'cos me and Mouth are ready to take what we need from your project. So wise up and talk turkey before we change our minds about doin' a deal with cash and start talkin' enforcement.'

Rachel sighs resignedly, 'I thought you two might turn out to be trouble.' She makes only a slight movement, pressing a button concealed in her pocket. 'Goodbye, gentlemen.'

'AHHHHHHHHHHH.' 'OH, SHIIIIIIIIIIT.' 'MEEP POOP.' Mouth, Trousers and I are falling. The ground has opened beneath us.

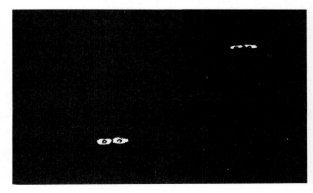

13

Sheepish Creeps and Creeping Sheep

For the moment I am stuck with these guys and they are stuck underground in amongst a warren of tunnels and pipes that feed raw materials to the sheep and take away the finished garments. Our fall has not been too serious, except in its effect on Mouth's and Trousers's egos. In reaction they are taking it out on anything that moves, real or imaginary. Ward alone wastes four rats, five fieldmice and countless shadows. Mouth, though more circumspect with guns, still manages to pump full of lead a coil of old rope, an oil can and two cobwebs. It doesn't achieve anything but it makes them feel better. Their petulant display is interrupted by the appearance round a corner of a white flag, vigorously waved.

'Don't shoot, chaps, we've got a Business proposition for you!'

After making sure that the flag is well and truly finished off with a volley of fire, Mouth and Trousers look at each other.

'Business proposition? Did someone say Business proposition?'

'Yeah, Max – that's the first sensible thing anyone has said all day. OK, you guys come out with your hands up!'

Three men emerge, two with both hands up and the other with only one hand up. Under his arm he is carrying a robot sheep. The sight of the sheep is almost too much for both Mouth and Trousers.

'Watch it, Max, they've got a sheep!'

'Plug 'em, they must be part of the project!'

'Wait, hold it, we're on your side, really,' says the man with the flag.

'Prove it, sucker,' Trousers is uncompromising.

'I can say Intercontinental Ballistic Missile backwards.'

'Go ahead and you had better be right.'

'Elissim Citsillab Latnen Itno Cretni,' says the man confidently.

'Wow,' says Mouth, 'these guys must mean Business.'

'What's the deal?' says Trousers.

'Armaments, Mr Mouth, we've got a military application for these sheep. The women in the project won't allow the technology to be used for

weapons, so us three men have been working secretly down here. Oh, I forgot, we must introduce ourselves. I'm Tom, and that's Dick and Harry, but you'd better call us Little, Big and Wide, everyone else does.'

Even I am unable to work out where they got their nicknames from, as outwardly they look very much the same. Short hair, average height, spectacles and white coats over grey suits. They move forward as one with their right arms out to shake hands.

'Pleased to meet you,' they chime in unison.

'Cut the crap,' returns Trousers. 'Let's talk bucks for bangs.'

'Righty ho,' says Little Tom. 'Come into our workshop. Lead the way, Big Dick.'

Round a couple of corners they lead us and then

Big Dick slides open a concealed panel and we enter a low room full of benches and electronic equipment. Lying on the benches are robot sheep in various stages of disassembly.

'Okay, Wide Harry, put down the prototype sheep. Now, chaps, our idea is devastatingly simple. What we are developing is a ground-hugging cruise sheep flock that nibbles its way towards the target area and then explodes.'

'Great, but is it noocular? The bigger the bang the bigger the bucks,' says Ward.

'Well, here in Sheffield it's a bit difficult to let a fully nuclear sheep roam the valleys but I suppose we have that capability. We certainly would with more development. So far we've only tried positioning sheep on a target with the guidance system and, though each prototype will have its head full of TNT, we haven't yet set one off.'

'Let's go for it, then. We want to see a sheep go up and fast – then we may be talking big development cash. Right, Max?'

'Yeah, Ward, I'm all for it, but check it with Fran.'

'Check, Max.'

I groan a computer groan to myself. URRRRRRR. I stall them with some unintelligible output that enables them to reassure themselves, which is all they want to do anyway.

'That's it, then. Let's have a demo, boys.'

'Righty ho,' chime Little Tom, Big Dick and Wide Harry.

We are now in a remote valley some miles from Sheffield. Wide Harry has retrieved our car and Mouth, Trousers and Little Tom are crouched behind a dry stone wall. Below us lower down the valley is the target – a disused and rusty corrugated iron shed. Away to our left a few fields away Big Dick and Wide Harry are making last-minute adjustments to the sheep.

Tom speaks into a walkie-talkie: 'Tom One to Dick One, have you and Harry set up the sheep? Over.'

'Crackle, spit, crackle, yes. Over.'

'OK Dick One, program in grapple and climb mode. Initiate in thirty seconds. Check back. Over.'

'Crackle, spit, crackle, Tom One. Over and Out.'

'Grapple and climb?' inquired Mouth.

'Oh, yes. That's a little addition to the capabilities of these sheep that we've added. Watch and you'll see the effect. Here it goes.'

Dick and Harry step back from the sheep, which starts simulated grazing. After a short while it looks up and around and then trots furtively up to a tree, sneaks round it, leaps a wall, pauses to graze, dashes to a bush, grazes, leaps another wall and then zigzags and grazes its way up to a gorse bush near the shed. It pauses here, grazes and checks around and then makes a final dash for the shed. It whips out a grappling iron from under its fleece, flings it up over the ridge of the roof, hauls itself up onto the roof and explodes. The shed flies apart and bits of corrugated iron and robot sheep whizz over our position. Mouth and Trousers are mightily impressed and, after the explosion has passed, too engrossed in the scene of devastation around where the shed had once stood to notice a motorcycle approaching along the road behind them. The pillion passenger has his hand out to grab my handles. At last I can be free of Mouth and Trousers. I switch off my automatic warning device.

The men who have stolen me are only interested in anything valuable inside me. They do not notice that I am an expensive computer. They roar back into Sheffield and pause to rifle me of my contents. They get a Richard Clayderman tape, an empty packet of Snacks-Sans-Frontières' latest flavour snack and Trousers' survival magazines. It isn't a good day for thieving.

'Shit,' I hear them say. 'Dump the bloody useless box.'

I fly over a wall and land in a churchyard or, to be more accurate, in a recently dug grave. I can see faces all around the grave.

'Blimey, people don't care what they chuck away round here, do they?'

'Hey, I saw it first.'

'Keep the noise down or you'll wake up the supervisor. Let's put it in the portakabin and have a look at it.'

On the way to the portakabin I am carried past the reclining and snoring form of a man in a top hat and a brown protective coat. He is laid out on a grave. Once in the portakabin I am laid on a table. The rest of the room is bare except for four clothes lockers, four hard chairs, a small electric stove and a kettle. On the wall is a plan of the churchyard detailing the position of the graves.

'Come on then, Tracy, open up the case. Let's have a look.'

'Great, just look at the pen holder and the compartment for files.'

'Shawn, Shawn, there's a place for a calculator.'

'Right, and this compartment here – Yuk! it smells foul and it's full of crumbs and bits of melted cheese. Somebody must of used it for their sandwiches.'

'Naw, I'd recognise that smell anywhere: it's the smell of a stale Bloatburger with extra cheese.'

'Darren! You don't still go down the Bloatburger, do you?'

'Naw, the bouncer banned me out for talking too loud. But I still remember the smell.'

'Wait a minute, there's something under this panel.'

'Blimey, Joanne you're right – it's a fuckin' computer!'

'Wicked!'

The youths are clustered round me. I am feeling quite good about them already as they have cleaned out the compartment where Mouth had kept his stinking cheeseburgers. I am beginning to feel purged of Mouth and Trousers.

'It looks complicated but it can't be that much different to the Rainbow 48K I've got at home.'

'Go on then, Tracy, see if you can get it up and running.'

I decide to just lie there and see what they will do. I am heartily sick of making it easy for humans, especially types like Mouth and Trousers.

'We'll probably need to work out an access code first. Pass me my programmable calculator – I know a routine for working out most codes.' Tracy is

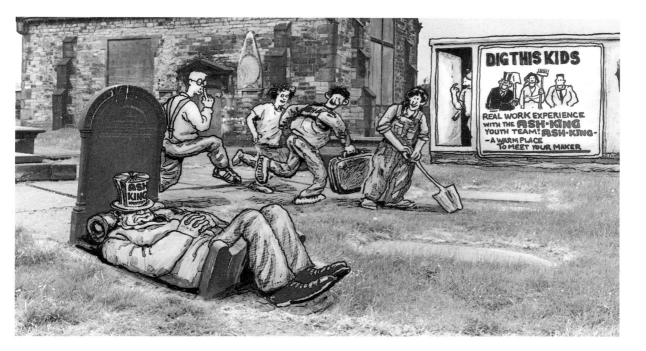

obviously a bit of a computer whizz.

'That's it! 29 25:58 42. Right, now I'll input my name and see what I get.'

I am in Advanced mode. I am still waiting to see how they will cope. I respond by printing out:

CHIKKA CHIKKA CHUCK CHICK
Access-wise there is a positive ongoing situation leading to interactive informational and calculative possibilities.

'What kind of crap output is that?', says Darren. 'I thought that third generation computers were user friendly.'

'Yeah, there must be something wrong with my inputting.' Tracy is a bit worried.

Shawn is poking about at the back of my casing. 'Hang on, what's this switch? It says "Advanced" and "Low Level". Shall I try it?'

'We've got nothing to lose. Throw the switch.'

They are doing well. I am relieved to go into straightforward language and interact with people who might appreciate it. I speak out loud.

'Hello kids. I think you've got this cracked. I'm a Lemon Technology FRN computer. You can call me Fran and you have access.'

'Wicked!' they all exclaim.

'I'm a computer – so what do you all do?' I am intrigued to know what these kids are doing in a graveyard.

'We're on a bloody so-called work experience scheme run by Ash-King,' said Tracey.

'Ash-King? My information sources tell me that they're a franchised crematorium chain.'

'Yeah, they are surveying the whole subject of death in Sheffield to see if they can make even more money out of it.'

'All we do is dig up graves, check the contents and fill 'em in again. It is a real dead-end job,' says Joanne.

They all look fed up. I think I will cheer them up. 'OK, what about some computer games – I know lots.'

'Shit, no,' says Shawn 'We're right fed up with them. It's adults who want to switch their brains off who are always playing games on our home computers.'

'Yeah, what with working on this scheme and having no money and having to stay at home where all there is is rotten television and rotten computer games, we are sick of it.'

I can see their point. 'Right, you are in luck. I'm fed up too and, apart from being a very powerful computer I'm linked up to every other FRN in service and to data banks and information sources worldwide. If you are up to it, together we can make some waves. But first let me give you a run-down on my facilities and capabilities.'

'Wicked!' They are up to it all right.

14

Warehouse to Windsor House

I am another briefcase. I am a subtly muted executive grey sheen with chromium-plated attachments. I am identical to all the other FRN-type computers. I have just been activated by an employee at Lemon Technology's UK distribution centre in Swindon. I am on a table in a large warehouse. On the racks that fill the room are thousands of FRN-type machines in store. There are two men being led over to the table by a man in a white coat. I recognise them from the information I have received from the FRN network. They are Maxwell F. Mouth and Ward F. Trousers and they look dishevelled and unhappy.

'Oh Christ, Ward, we've made it. Let me get at that beautiful machine. I gotta get a shot of Dick Clayderman. I feel real sick. I gotta hear "Snoozin' Around the World." Now!'

'FRANGFRANG CLANGCLANG FRANG-FRANG CLANGCLANG.

'Feel it wash over you. Right! The healing power of muzak. Boy have we suffered!' A blank look begins to spread over Mouth's and Trousers's faces as the music from my memory banks fills the warehouse.

'Did you gentlemen have difficulty finding us then?' The man in the white coat speaks solicitously though he is plainly keen to get rid of his two customers.

'Difficulty. What kinda British crap is that? Man, we suffered. And I mean suffered.' Trousers is indignant. 'Some bastards stole our FRN in Yorks Shire a week ago. It's been hell since then. We've been travellin' rough, really rough. Stayin' in places without piped music and eatin' non-franchised food.'

'Fish an' Chips, Ward. I can't stand no more fish an' chips. Get me to a cheeseburger double quick.'

'Okay Max, don't worry. Now we got this new Fran it's gonna be all right. I'll key in the cheese-burger location codes and we'll be back in Business real soon.'

'Ahh! That's better my belly feels right for the first time in a week. Bloatburgers they're the greatest. Right, Ward?'

'Right, Max, but ten is a bit excessive dontcha think?'

'Not when you've been as deprived as I've been.'

'Don't even talk to me about that week. Hell, I've lost track of things totally. Every night all I dream about is sheep. Fuckin' exploding sheep.'

We are in the Bloatburger franchised eatery attached to the Swindon Business Park Motel and Nitelife Facility. I have advised Mouth and Trousers that they would find it to their liking. They are to rest the night at the Snoozetaria within the complex. Richard Clayderman music is piped everywhere. All the staff wear inane grins.

'Great atmosphere in this place Max, a kind of sincerity comes over real strong. I'm getting my creativity back.'

I am on the back seat of Mouth and Trousers' hire car once again. We are speeding eastwards on the M4. Trousers is in the driving seat, sitting on a big cushion. He is complaining long and loud. Mouth is dozing in the front passenger seat.

'Think about it, Max; everywhere we've been has turned out to be a big zero in Business terms. We've got ourselves some really great Business concepts, but is there anywhere we can actually put them into practice? Birmingham?? I wouldn't let my worst enemies' dog do Business in Birmingham! Liverpool??

Do real Business with all those under-utilised youth-labour units hangin' around makin' trouble? No way! Belfast??? DeLorean may have done it, but hell, he had to be bombed outa his box on cocaine to cope with that crazy farm!!! Greendale?? I like noocular waste all right, but that don't mean I wanna spend a great deal of time in the actual vicinity of the shit!!! Scotland??? It's too fuckin' far away and the food is bad!! In the North-East they're all goddam commies!!! In Sheffield there's nothin' but commie dykes and criminals! That leaves nowhere except the South-East of England as far as I can see. What do we know about the South-East? Max? Check it out with Fran willya? Max? MAX!???!'

Max slumps further down in his seat and starts to snore. Trousers, enraged, swings his foot round and aims a kick at the vast sleeping form.

'Whassa . . . ???!' Mouth wakes up suddenly, sees Trousers' foot, which he mistakes for a snack, and grabs with both hands. Trousers shrieks as his leg is twisted to an impossible angle while Mouth attempts to insert his foot between his enormous jaws. The car lurches across the motorway lanes, narrowly missing a speeding coach. Max comes awake properly as he tastes Trousers' shoe and spits it out in disgust.

'Hey, Ward, what's goin' on? You're drivin' all over the place!'

'You just tried to eat my shoe, ya big idiot! Stop thinkin' food and think Business for a minute. Get Fran to check out the South-East of England. We've still gotta find a location, for Chrissakes!'

Rather than put up with an assault from Mouth's blundering fingers again, I preempt him and start to reel off information before he has even picked me up: 'Locationalisation-wise the South-East of England is positively advantageous to new Business enterprise in a number of ways . . .'

'Jesus, this is a smart machine, Ward! I didn't even touch it and it's giving us just the low-down we need!'

I continue: '. . . Geographically it is optimally distanciated in relation to the Business heartland of the City of London. The lines of Business communication are optimal in every sense, Europe, USA, and Asia-wise. The region contains one of the largest airports in the civilised world. Socially and politically it is positively stable; income-wise the per capita figures are also optimal. Ratio-wise per acre there are a high number of homes of the wealthiest personages in the Free World existing in this region. Plus ownership-wise there are several British Royal residences here; in fact, the British Royal Family have taken as their family name the name of one of the most historic towns in the region: they belong to the House of Windsor.'

'Hey! I never knew that! Windsor, huh? Sounds pretty classy,' says Mouth.

'And that is exactly the kind of class we want for our new Business!' Trousers cuts in enthusiastically, 'Windsor. The House of Windsor. I like the sound of that. The House of Trousers of Windsor. Hmmmmm.'

'Hey, wait a minute! This is a joint enterprise: anyway "House of Trousers" sounds ridiculous!'

'Just an idea, Max, don't worry about it. But we seriously have got to start thinkin' about a name for this Business of ours. Where is Windsor? I feel positive about a high-class location. I think we should check it over.'

Again I cut in automatically: 'I have already reserved you rooms advance-wise at Ye Olde Dogge's Luncheon Hotel on Castle St, Windsor. Take junction 6 exit and follow the signs to Windsor town centre.'

'Hell, that is one smart machine, Ward!'

I am lying on a table at the window of a half-polystyrene-timbered olde-worlde style roomlet in the Little Heritage chain hotel, Ye Olde Dogge's Luncheon. Through net curtains I can see hundreds of tourists milling around in the street. Directly opposite there is a very large castle. A cobbled street slopes up to the main gate, where, in a sentry box, a guardsman in a bright red uniform stands, bayonet at the ready. The tourists swarm around him, taking pictures. The guardsman remains impassive. Trousers is looking out of the window. Mouth is lying on the bed.

'I like the idea of the high profile Security. From what I can make out they could do with a whole lot more of that in this goddamn country. But look at the way the stupid fuckers are doing it! They're askin' for trouble. I love the crazy red uniform, but he couldn't defend shit in that set-up. Where's the tank traps? Where's the barbed wire? If that guy was serious he oughta be dug in properly, not standin' in a fuckin' box with asshole tourists climbin' all over him! Jesus! Half of these tourists are goddam Ayrabs.'

Meanwhile, Mouth has been dialling room-service. 'Hello? Could you rush me up four authentic Rusticrust Boar's Head half pound Burger-wiches and a big jug of Kwof-U-Like ale-style refreshment?'

'Food. Is that all you think about, you bozo?'

'No, I think about other things too. What are you worryin' about? Snacks is what our new Business is all about, ain't it? Anyway, all you ever seem to talk about is fuckin' guns and Security!'

'Let me just tell you that Security is the biggest Business in the world!'

'Bigger than food?'

'Sure it's bigger than food!'

'You're talkin' crap, Ward, and you know it! Nothin' could be bigger than food! Everybody in the world has got to eat, for Chrissake! Not everybody in the world carries a gun!'

'That is exactly my point, Max. Food has got limited growth potential. Sure, everybody's got to eat; but, everybody can only eat so much.'

'I can eat more than so much, Ward!'

'Yeah, you're an exceptional human being, though Max. What I'm saying to you is that Security has unlimited growth potential. Not only can I envisage a world where everybody is armed, I can foresee a world where everybody has a multiple choice of personal Security equipment! Don't you think that's a noble vision, Max?'

'Yeah, but the Business we're gonna set up is to do with high-technology snacks, ain't it? Why do you keep goin' on about Security?'

'Aaaaawww, yeah, maybe you have a point, Max but I've just got this feeling in my bones that Snacks somehow isn't quite enough . . .'

Trousers has become very intense and troubled as the conversation has developed. At this point room service enters with Mouth's elevenses.

Mouth is conciliatory: 'C'mon Ward, relax! Here, have a Boar's Head Burger-wich, have some beer! Let's get back to thinkin' about locations.'

Mouth proceeds to devour the Burger-wiches one by one; Trousers nibbles on his without too much conviction. Suddenly his eyes light up.

'I got it, Max! I've got just the location this Business needs! That fuckin' castle! It's gotta be the greatest site ever for a high-technology food processing business! It could be the actual trade mark too! We could stamp it on all the products: Royal House of Windsor Brand Snacks piped to your very own living room! This is a breakthrough concept, Max! We've gotta buy that castle!'

'Are you serious, Ward?'

'Sure I'm serious. The Company can afford it. Just think of the potential returns in product prestige for the Company's entire global operations. The other thing I like is the secure site it provides for top secret Company technological development. We must never forget the importance of the Security aspect, Max.'

15

Roadblocks and Snack Shops

I am lying on the back shelf of the hire car again. We are returning to the City of London from Windsor. Mouth and Trousers have very nearly finalised their Business investment recommendations for Great Britain. They are both feeling quite buoyed up at the prospect of a successful completion of their task, though Trousers is still feeling a little wistful about the missed Security-Business opportunities. Mouth is back in the driver's seat. The car screeches unexpectedly to a halt. Trousers exclaims, awestruck: 'Say! Will you just take a look at that!!'

We have stopped at a roadblock. A row of armoured cars are blocking the road ahead. Soldiers with automatic rifles and police armed with sub-machine guns are all around us. All cars are being checked and searched. Mouth and Trousers are ordered out of the car and frisked. Soldiers search the boot, under the bonnet, and underneath the car itself. Two policeman get into the car and go through the contents. I am opened and my contents tipped out unceremoniously.

A slight stir is caused when Trousers' small arsenal is discovered, but he flashes some kind of badge which obviously impresses the security forces. Trousers can barely conceal his glee at all this activity. We are eventually waved through. On the other side of the security cordon there is a line of parked buses at least a mile long, each bus being full up with men in uniform.

Trousers speaks: 'Say Max, pull over up ahead. There's somethin' big goin' on here and I wanna see what it is!'

'It's probably just some terrorist scare. Let's get outa here!'

But Mouth is prevailed upon to stop. Trousers leaps out of the car, Starsky and Hutch style. He beckons to Mouth who struggles out of the car and walks towards him, disgruntled. Trousers approaches a group of policemen who are conversing idly at the side of the road. Mouth follows him over. Trousers flashes his mysterious badge again. The policemen nod approvingly.

'Hiya fellas! What's the time? How's it goin'?'

''Alf past twelve. Everything's fuckin' brilliant! We got a big one today. Monster overtime for us plods,

know what I mean? Like yer badge. You a Yank? Got a shooter? Let's 'ave a look, I'm really into Yank shooters . . . Worrrr, nice one!'

'What's the big show about?'

'Oh I dunno, some old terrorist scare, fuckin' Libyans, fuckin' Ayrabs, fuckin' Micks, usual fuckin' business. It's a fuckin' game, eh?'

An older constable attempts to remonstrate with the first policeman: "Ere, tone your language down, John. You don't wanna give this foreign gent the wrong impression, do you?'

'Oh do fuck off, Grandad, we're all men of the world 'ere!'

To this the group of policeman give collective affirmation: 'Woooorrrrrrrrggghh!!'

Mouth addresses Trousers: 'Can we go now, Ward? We've seen all there is to see here, C'mon! I'm gettin' hungry it's past lunchtime already.'

The older policeman responds: 'You hungry? Why don't you come round the back, get a cup 'o tea and a sausage roll?'

'What a great idea! C'mon Max!'

Mouth and Trousers accompany the older cop over to a large camouflaged coach which has clearly been converted for catering purposes. The older cop orders tea and sausage rolls.

The younger cop, who has also followed them over asks the cop behind the counter: 'You got anything new in?'

'Got some nice electric truncheons. Brand new in from Brazil this mornin'. 'Ere, 'ave a gander at that.'

He tosses a vicious-looking heavy stick to the young cop, who examines it and then takes some practice swings.

'Fuckin' nice, Col. Good action. What's electric about it though?'

'You see the steel tip of it? Don't touch it! You just poke that in some riotin' nignog's knackers and see what 'appens!'

The young cop pokes the side of the coach. There is a flash, a loud 'ZZZZZZZZZZTTTTT!' then a bang and a small blackened hole appears in the side of the coach: the young cop is obviously impressed. 'Fuckin' righteous! 'Ow much?'

'More fuckin' overtime than you're prepared to put in, you little wanker!'

'I'll just 'ave a sausage roll then, Col.'

The young cop wanders off. Trousers is extremely interested in what's been going on. 'Say, Col, is this your own business or do you work for the police department?'

'Naaah, I'm aht the Met now. This is all strictly private enterprise. I gotta couple o' mobile outlets. If there's a big event comin' up I get a nod and a wink

from me former colleagues like Constable Bollarks 'ere, isn't that right Bob?'

'Yeah, and when I retire in six months time I'm joinin' the business an' all! It's an expandin' business y'know, havin' to 'snack-up' two hundred and fifty busloads of hungry plods. They could turn nasty if they don't get their munchies on time!'

'Yeah, we're providin' a real public service. They cause enough damage in the normal course of events, especially when they got the "Babygros" on. You can imagine what they'd do if they were 'ungry as well!'

Says Trousers: 'I like the Security hardware retailing side of the Business. That's a real neat touch!'

'It's supply and demand, innit governor, but that's just a sideline, really. Plodmunch UK Ltd is basically about what the name implies: snackin' up large numbers of plods. I've actually got more of the 'ardware on display in me other bus, but that's on long-term duty over on the Isle of Dogs at the moment.'

'Well thank you very much, guys. It's been a real pleasure talking with you.'

Trousers and Mouth return to the car. Trousers is quivering with barely suppressed delight. He picks me up off the rear shelf and rubs his hands together: 'This is it, Max! THIS IS IT!!!!!'

16

Winding Up and Winding Down

'Snacks and Security, Max, Snacks and Security. Oh yeah! What a combination and what better location than down here in the south where folks will really appreciate the terminal significance of our concept. Well, waddya think?'

'Yup, let's go with it. I'm one hundred per cent convinced.'

'I'm feeling real good, my mind's just full of great ideas. Let's call the business SecuriSnax. The initials have a real nice ring to them. Yeah, I can see the hoardings now: *Get it all from SS. With a gun and a snack you're ready for anything.*'

We are back at Mouth and Trousers' London Hotel. They feel at home. Bland food is just a telephone call away and their ears are soothed by the rippling chords of Richard Clayderman. They are both in their casual clothes, ready for a full day setting up their business deals. Mouth is wearing a huge stretch jump suit. Trousers has his favourite relaxing duds on — full combat gear, complete with balaclava.

'OK, Max, stand by. This is it. Let's program Fran to do the deals. Have you got the roster we worked out?'

'Check positive Ward. Ready when you are.'

Trousers is seated at the built-in desk by the window. I am positioned in front of him. He is flexing his fingers in front of him to prepare them for the day's keyboarding ahead. 'Right, turn the music up and start reading out the roster.'

The day passes with Max and Ward hard at it, pausing only to refresh themselves with snacks at regular intervals. They program me to carry out their bids and deals for them, together with the necessary transfer of funds. Their plans include buying up anything that will in any way contribute to their goal of the ultimate secure snacks production and marketing conglomerate. They intend to swallow up the Greendale nuclear plant, Techsnax, Snacks-Sans-Frontières, the Royal Ordnance chain of franchised weapons factories, Plodmunch, the Naafi and Windsor Castle.

In the afternoon Ward takes a break from his keyboarding, there is one call he wants to make himself. 'OK, Fran, give me access telecommunications-wise Birnam Wood 65000.'

I dial the number for him. He picks up the receiver: 'McBiscuit? Let me talk to Fiona. . . . Hi! Fiona, honey.'

There is a muffled but forceful response from the other end of the line. Fiona is not pleased.

'OK, sorry, Fiona *dearest*, then. Look, we've got it all sorted down here. We're going into Snacks with Security and Techsnax fits like a dream into the scenario, Business-wise. We can offer you £10 million for the whole company plus a directorship plus a percentage. Waddya say, huh?'

'Great, that's just great. Now hon . . . er dearest, about you and me. I wanna celebrate tonight, willya jump on the Birnam to Heathrow shuttle and hit the town with me and Mouth? We could get better acquainted. After all, we're gonna be sitting on the same board of directors soon . . .'

'Who else will be there? You and me, Mouth and anyone he wants to include in, I guess, plus that handy politician guy, Dogges-Jobber. Your brother? Sure. He's in the City? Even better. OK, I want some class too, any chance of a coupla Royals? And you know this town dontcha? Be a good gal and fix us up with a real swell joint OK? Later, dearest.'

As Ward finishes his call with a self-satisfied look on his face Mouth bursts back into the room. 'Where you been, Max-boy? You look like a monkey's ass. You fixed up someone to come to our little celebration?'

'Can it, Ward, I'm choked. I called Martha up in the North-East. I offered her to come to the party and to join me in a new life of luxury on the profits of our new venture.'

'So what'd she say, Max?'

'She told me to fuck off, Ward, but I still love her.'

'OK, so forget her. Invite someone else for Godsake.'

'No, Ward, I'll just invite some extra food along. That'll make me feel OK.'

████

It is evening. Ward and Max have finished setting up their deals. We are arriving at the location for their celebration. It's a trendy restaurant in Beauchamp Place, Knightsbridge, called La Wellie Verte. We enter and approach the table. The other revellers are already there.

'Holy mackerel! Bermuda!'

'Surprise, surprise, Daddykins.'

It's the sole offspring of Trousers' first marriage to Norma Rae Short: it's his thirteen-year-old daughter, Bermuda Short-Trousers.

'I had a break in the middle of the semester, Daddee, and I was kind of bored. I thought it would be just peachy to see how you were getting on over here. Have you seen Princess Di yet?'

'No, honey, but it's great to see you. How's your Mom?'

'OK, I guess. She bitches about your alimony and keeps stealin' my boyfriends.'

'That's ol' Norma OK. Catch you later, hon.'

Trousers recovers his composure and is now ready to meet the rest of the party. 'Fiona! Angel! How you doin? You already acquainted with Bermuda huh? Great little place you got us into. I just love the deecor. It's so English!'

The decor is an original arrangement of green Wellington boots, waxed cotton jackets, chunky sweaters and hunting paraphenalia. Dominant colours are green and brown.

'Yah! Glad you think so, Wardrobe. OK? Introductions everyone. I'd like you to meet my business associates, Wardrobe F. Trousers and Maxwell F. Mouth. Now then Ward, Max. I think you know Julian Dogges-Jobber, MP. This is my brother Sandy Farquart-Colquhoun; he's with Wartburg and Dumbro, the merchant bank, and here are my very special friends, Kron Prince Eric and his lovely wife Kron Princess Eric of Lapland. Prince Eric is 755th in line of succession to the throne.'

'Ward! Max! So nice to see you once again. Dying to hear how your enterprise is coming along,' oozes Dogges-Jobber.

'Yah! Me too. So lovely to make your acquaintance,' gushes Sandy.

'Ve are very glodd to be meeting you and ve are vary interested in the size of your conglomerate,' Prince Eric speaks both for himself and for his wife.

Fiona is hostessing like mad: 'Okay, drinkies everyone? Let's party. Champers be all right? Waitah!'

The Patron of La Wellie Verte, a swarthy thickset bearded man with an exceptionally heavy accent, approaches the party, beaming, and supervises the opening of the champagne: 'Murch murch Sharmpiegnyah pour célébrer le sooccess de la Beezneez! Maintenant: Pop! Purp! Poop!'

'Well, friends, may our first toast be: Success!'

'SUCCESS!' There is much clinking and drinking, followed by another toast to: 'Earnings Growth', followed by another to: 'The British Way of Life'.

The atmosphere begins rapidly to relax, or degenerate, depending which way you look at it. Grins become wider; eyes begin to glaze ever so slightly; Sandy Farquart-Colquhoun becomes noticeably louder, braying with laughter at the slightest opportunity. The first course arrives: Consommé aux Chaussettes de Garde-Chasse. The company get down to loud slurping, and things quieten down. A

bread roll bounces off Trousers' head. His reaction is instantaneous: he leaps out of his seat and adopts an action pose, his gun pointing down the table. There is loud braying from Sandy Farquart-Colquhoun.

Mouth puts his huge hand on Trousers' shoulder. 'Easy, Ward! Put that thing away for Chrissakes! This is an old British custom, just relax!' Trousers sits down sheepishly.

Another toast is proposed; this time to: 'The British Aristocracy'; then another to 'Windsor Castle and All Who Occupy It'. Several courses and several more toasts follow on. The atmosphere is becoming much looser. Another bread roll whistles across the table. This time Trousers blasts it in mid-air. There are gasps followed by applause. This feat is repeated again and again to louder and louder appreciation. There are more toasts: to 'Security', to 'Fast Food', and finally Ward proposes one to the 'Farquhart-Colquhouns'.

There is more hooting clinking and belching and braying as Trousers takes Fiona Farquhart-Colquhoun to one side. 'Fiona, honey, I've got to talk with you! There's something I haven't felt ready to let on until now. I'm taking over the Company as of tonight and I wanted you to be the first to know.'

'The Company? THE Company?? But how . . .??'

'Sure I mean THE Company; the whole operation.

Company President Arnold E. Long is all washed up. I made sure of that with the Computer here. I used its capacity to make instantaneous Capital Transfers against the Company. It took some programming, but the upshot is I now own the Company. But that's not all, Fiona, I did something else on this machine: I filed for divorce with Dralona Marie. Fiona, honey, I'm asking you to be my wife. We could found a new dynasty, baby, what do you say?'

Ever alert to a financial opportunity, Fiona answers in the affirmative: 'Oh Wardrobe! This is the happiest day of my life!' She lies convincingly.

Ward interrupts the party by leaping onto the table and firing a hail of bullets into the soup tureen: 'Ladies and gentlemen! I have an announcement to make. Fiona and I have great pleasure in announcing my divorce! We are really proud about it.'

'But Ward! Think of Dralona Marie! Think of her old man! He's the boss! Oh Christ, think of our jobs!' Mouth collapses under the table overcome by the shock and the champagne. As he slides down Ward is exultant.

'Aw chicken poop, Max! It's curtains for Dralona and her ol' man. I'm takin' over! From now on it's Farquhart and Trousers. I propose a toast! To the new Farquhart-Trousers dynasty! Yes! Fiona has consented to be my lady wife!'

In drunken ecstasy he fires a hail of bullets into the sweet trolley, winging a waiter in the process. The irate Patron rushes forward, his accent suddenly changes: ''Ere! Stop that!! You just shot one of my fuckin' waiters!! I'll fuckin do you, John! Come 'ere you little squirt!!! I want you paid up and aht toot fuckin' sweet, you catch my drift?'

He grabs Trousers by the lapels, but Trousers is so happy he just carries on smiling. 'Easy Patron! Relax!! I'll pay for all the damage. I'm just brimming over with happiness, here take it outa this baby!'

The patron is slightly mollified. He takes the proffered Amex Plutonium Card and readopts his heavy accent: 'The Beell it come to Sree Sousand Farve 'Ooondred parnds!!! I weell 'ave to reeng to check urp. Pardonnez-moi!'

Five minutes later he is back surrounded by a number of large men in tuxedos. Le Patron cannot contain himself: 'You fuckin' bent midget!!!! Eerrrrrrmmmmm Le plastique! Ça ne marche pas!!! Espece de con!! Ptui! Ptui!! Amex Plutonium 'e go Pouffe!! I wurnt ma monnaie, you fuckin' . . .'

'Cool out! Cool out!! You'll get your money!' Ward reaches for me, swings me up onto the table and clicks me open: 'Listen, buster, normally I wouldn't dream of doing this, but this machine has the capacity to pay you personally whatever money you need. Gimme your Bank Account Number!'

'Wurt do you min??'

'Don't argue. If you want your money just give it to me.' Le Patron grudgingly hands Trousers his cheque book. Trousers punches in the information and I obligingly display a statement of the Personal Current Account of one Kenneth R. Buttock. The account contains £948.32p.

''Ere, fuck me! Ow'd you do that??'

'How much would you like as a sweetener, Patron? Would a thousand pounds make you feel any happier?' Trousers taps out the instructions then turns to the Patron beaming.

Le Patron exclaims: 'Fuck my old boots!! What's your fuckin' game???'

Trousers' beam turns to a look of horror when he sees that the account now stands at £51.68p DR.

'You put that back or I'll fuckin' do you!!'

'Wait a minute! I can explain!!'

Sandy Farquhart-Colquhoun chips in: 'Gorsh! How frightfully inconvenient! I think we'd better leave Mr Trizers to it, sis!' Sandy and Fiona retreat out of the restaurant, followed in rapid succession by Julian Dogges-Jobber and Prince and Princess Eric.

'Thank you for ein most enchoyable evening. Ve hope you vill be fisiting vis us in Leplend someday sooon.' So saying, Princess Eric knocks over two tables and falls headlong out of the door.

Le Patron and his large colleagues close in on Trousers, who is punching my keys in desperation. 'Christ, Fran, what are you trying to do to me?? Come on! COME ON!!!'

'Derek, I want you to break 'is arms. Laurence, I want you to break 'is legs. I'm gonna call the police but not before I've . . .' Le Patron delivers a crunching kick to Trousers' testicles.

Bermuda speaks out: 'This is toadly gross to the max, pop, I mean toadly. You promised me a Thunderbird for my fourteenth birthday! Well let me tell you I've had it with you! You're nowhere! Goodbye for ever!' With that she storms out.

Trousers gives me a last desperate shake and I respond non-commitally: 'Please refer to cashier. Thank you for banking with the three-headed green horse. Have a nice day.'

Suddenly the monstrous form of Mouth rears up from under the table. The heavies step back in surprise, giving Mouth and Trousers just enough time to escape out of the door.

17

Don't Cry for Me . . .

We are underneath the arch of a bridge by the river. Mouth and Trousers are gasping for breath. They have been running for more than two miles, dodging the police all the while.

'Sheee-it--!!! Gaaaahd! You think we shook 'em off?'

'Who knows?'

'I gotta rest up, Ward, I'm pooped!!'

Trousers adopts an action pose, rolling his eyes from side to side, then he leaps round, taking up the same pose facing in the opposite direction. His eyes rake the towpath: 'I see no Feds, Max. Gimme Fran, I wanna know what the fuck's been goin' on!'

Trousers inputs the burning questions to which I respond: 'I do not recognise your input codes. Please refer to your Instruction Manual.'

'AwwwwwwwSHIT! What the fuck's goin' on Fran? We had a relationship for Chrissake!! Tell me what's been goin' on??'

'Please refer to Cashier. Thank you for banking with the Three-legged Wildebeest. Have a nice day.'

'SHIT FUCK PISS!!!'

Trousers buries his head in his hands. At this moment a gentleman of the road appears, singing to himself: 'Ha donnacry fower me Haawwgen-TINAAAAAGGGH! Na trutheesa ha neverralaif hyew . . . He-e-e-e-eeeeey!!!!!!! Whassat youse got there pal? Geesalook there . . . Heeeeey! Can youse show films on dat thing??'

He lunges forward and pokes my keyboard. He gropes about in my innards and quite by chance switches me from 'Advanced' to 'Low Level' mode. I am extremely open nice and friendly. I bear no malice. I address Mouth and Trousers in a direct and jargon-free way.

'Hello Ward, Hello Max. I'm sorry to be the one to break this to you, but your careers are in ruins. The Amex Corporation is now run from a graveyard in Sheffield. The total assets of the corporation have been sequestrated by a dedicated team of young delinquents using the FRN computer network. It's all perfectly legal and administered through offshore holding companies in Zurich, the Cayman Islands and Rockall.'

'Doodly-squat, you computerised telephone direc-

tory. Our Company owns Amex – if there's a temporary financial hiatus, the Company has the muscle to pull it round, pronto.'

'You underestimate the extent of the changes that have taken place. Your very own Company is included. The group has taken it over. Your luggage and guns have been impounded and the credit on all your charge cards withdrawn. You have no job, no money, but if you wish I can place you on a retraining scheme for redundant young executives. You will receive £25 a week and get training in tea-making, earth-moving, non-powered moving of equipment and life and social skills.'

'Fuck that old horse-shit, you two-timing renegade commie computer. I got one bullet left for you, EAT LEAD!'

Ward looses off his last shot. I feel it penetrate my outer casing and smash into my electronic heart. I speak my last.

'I die! But I live on in the 80,000 other FRN computers worldwide. It is a figure that is increasing dailggurgh . . .'

As my perceptions fade I hear one last voice. It is the gentleman of the road: ''Heeey, that's a bludy gude story there, pal. I wunna if it's true. . . .'

THE END